Doctor,
I want to be the
fairest of them all!

Dr. Olivier Courtin-Clarins

Illustrated by Soledad Bravi

Doctor, I want to be the fairest of them all!

CLARINS

Contents

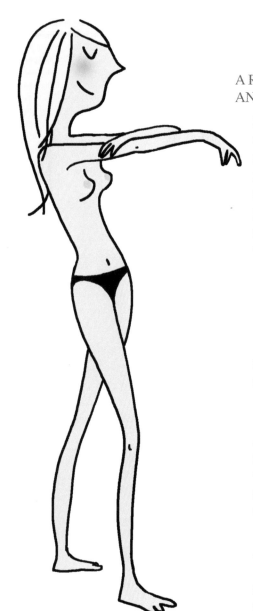

"Providing beauty advice has always been part of the CLARINS DNA".

Every woman is unique and special and has a beauty balance which is essential to her well-being. Women appreciate good advice and guidance, want to be loved and shown a path to their personal beauty. Each one of them deserves to be at their most beautiful. In constant contact with woman and listening to their needs and expectations, I decided, in honor of the 60th anniversary of our brand, to return to the heart of CLARINS and specifically address the concerns of today's women, by responding directly to beauty questions sent to us from journalists and women bloggers around the world. This quest led to women asking personal questions about their beauty needs in the hope of getting simple solutions adapted to their modern active lives to optimize their beauty and their attitudes in all situations (during the day, at night, at social events, last minute invitations…).

This book is a reflection of my appreciation of women, their beauty, their bodies, their bursts of laughter, their smiles and their *joie de vivre*. In responding to their myriad questions, this book will allow me to accompany them the best way I can through their daily lives to help contribute to their being conscious of how they can best live every moment to the fullest.

Living a serene life, feeling at one with ourselves, feeling loved and savoring every minute, every event, every happening, every emotion, our contentment influencing our well-being as well as that of those around us.

Your face tells it all. What a pleasure it is to see life's contentment harmoniously written there making it appear so happy... Over time our faces reflect who we are. They are an expression of ourselves, and reveal our personalities.

To feel beautiful, to be sure of your beauty, to feel good and in control of your body, to feel comfortable in your own skin, is being confident, content with life and the people around you, your friends, your family and your colleagues.
It's your own special way of being happy and spreading love and joy.

The five essential factors and elements which effect beauty are preventive health care through a balanced diet, the impacts of stress (both positive and negative), physical exercise, energy, resilience and well-being. These are all key to living a healthy life. For this reason, you will find in this book, not only beauty tips but also exercises and recommendations from CLARINS which, if followed regularly and with a smile, will bring immediate and long-term results.

CLARINS makes life more beautiful. This book is for you.

Dr. Olivier COURTIN-CLARINS

1
A REGAL BEARING AND (FOR) EVER YOUTHFUL

"You're positively glowing this morning!" is a compliment we'd love to hear on a regular basis.
You had a wonderful evening or you tried a new facial treatment... and it shows!

Your face reflects everything you sense and feel **because skin expresses your state of mind:**
-wrinkling your face, such as frowning and scowling causes lines;
-stress and poor breathing changes its look;
-fatigue and a hectic lifestyle contribute to premature ageing.

Listening to your skin and understanding it allows you to better take care of it. And **the younger you are when you start the longer you stay young.**

Facial beauty routine

Every morning:

1 Rid your skin of dirt and night secretions using a cotton pad soaked with a milk or lotion make-up remover.

2 On cleansed skin, moisturize your face. This important step allows the skin to fight against daily aggressions: UV rays, wind, cold, pollution, humidity.

3 When you apply your day (and night!) cream, include the neck and chest: the neck is a fragile area, especially when you've got sensitive skin that could show marks prematurely.

4 Apply an eye contour product to protect this fragile area.

① clean your face

② moisturize

③ don't forget your neck or your chest

④ apply an eye contour product

As often as possible:

1 Relax your face. When you're tense, without even realizing it, you clench your jaw and scowl. As a result, your face is marked by a frown and pursed lips... As soon as you think about relaxing, your features will relax it's automatic.

So, adopt this new beauty ritual, relax your features several times a day: your face will be brighter and more serene. Unwind. Treat yourself to a short break of a few minutes several times in your marathon day, become conscious of your breathing (p. 38) while "thinking positively", this will promote better cellular oxygenation which makes your complexion shine.

2 Invigorate your skin by spraying your face and even your hair with a jet of cold water just before turning the shower off.

① *relax and unwind*

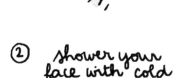

② *shower your face with cold water*

Every night:

1 Remove your eye and face make-up thoroughly without forgetting your neck.

2 Fight dark circles and puffiness by applying a care product on the contours which will stimulate blood and lymphatic circulation during the night.

3 Apply a night cream, because while you sleep, the skin goes into 'repair' mode and its natural cell renewal mechanism is working at a maximum. Your skin is more receptive to treatments at night because the secretion of sebum decreases during sleep, so the epidermis absorbs things better.

If you still have cream on your hands after applying it to your face, instead of wiping it off, use it... as a hand cream!

① *thoroughly remove make up*

② *apply an eye contour product*

③ *night cream*

Several times a week:

1 Exfoliate your skin to remove dead cells and activate cell regeneration. Over time, the ascent of cells to the surface of the skin slows down, resulting in a thinning of the epidermis.

2 Use a foaming, water-based facial cleanser several times a week to sanitize your skin, in addition to your make-up removal routine.

Exfoliating reduces wrinkling!
The right rhythm ? With skin that tends to be dry: exfoliate every 2 days. With skin that tends to be oily: once a week so as not to over activate the sebaceous glands. With mixed skin: 2 times a week, targeting a middle ground.

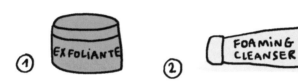

Whenever you can:

1 Make an appointment at your beauty salon for a thorough skin cleansing followed by a deep treatment. A beautician, a real skin professional, can evaluate the status and specific needs of your skin.

2 Soften your lips with a special ritual: exfoliating + mask + a replenishing balm.

Cleansing

Of all the beauty treatments, cleansing is the youth serum "par excellence". In a single process, you can rid your skin of cosmetics and cream residue and, very important, pollutants which settle on your skin during the day, hence the importance of cleansing, even if you don't wear make-up. It's essential to do it right:

- incomplete cleansing suffocates the skin through clogged pores, and leads to blackheads and a dull complexion;
- too rigorous a cleansing dries out and weakens the skin.

Inspired by treatments used at Clarins skin spas, this special cleansing routine removes, lifts up and eliminates all impurities without inflaming or irritating the skin. Use it at night and in the morning.

1 Warm the cleansing cream in the palm of your hands until it is at skin temperature.
2 Apply it with the entire surface of your hands by simply patting your hands on your face, without applying any pressure but by simply putting your hands flat on your face.
3 Don't forget your neck.
4 Pull your hands away as quickly as possible, as if your skin was burning. Repeat this gesture 5 or 6 times: as the cleansing cream thickens, it creates suction which pulls the make-up and impurities off without dislodging or irritating the tissue.
5 Rinse or wipe your face.
6 Finish by applying a lotion to remove the last residues of the cleansing cream. Applying a lotion is essential as it will rid your skin of the harmful effects of hard water.

Optimize the benefits of each treatment
Smell each cream before applying it.

Set yourself some achievable objectives
for the short term, in all areas of your life. Success and personal satisfaction brighten up facial expressions.

HELLO DOCTOR?

Will I have the same type of skin my whole life?

faq **1** No, it will adjust in response to life cycles (adolescence, pregnancy...), changes in lifestyle (changes in climate, new eating habits...) and the level of stress. So stay tuned in to your skin!

At what age should I start using an anti-wrinkle product?

faq **2** Getting into the habit of moisturizing your skin from the age of 20 is already preserving its youthfulness!

What's the difference between an anti-ageing and an anti-wrinkle product?

faq **3** An anti-wrinkle product works on facial lines, it protects and moisturizes the skin by providing a targeted response against wrinkles. An anti-ageing product is more general, addressing all the factors of ageing (sagging skin, dullness, spots).

Should I change my face cream with the seasons?

faq ❹ Not necessarily the type of cream, but the texture, yes! Use lighter ones in the summer, thicker ones in the winter. And as the seasons change, think of using serums – treatment effectiveness boosters.

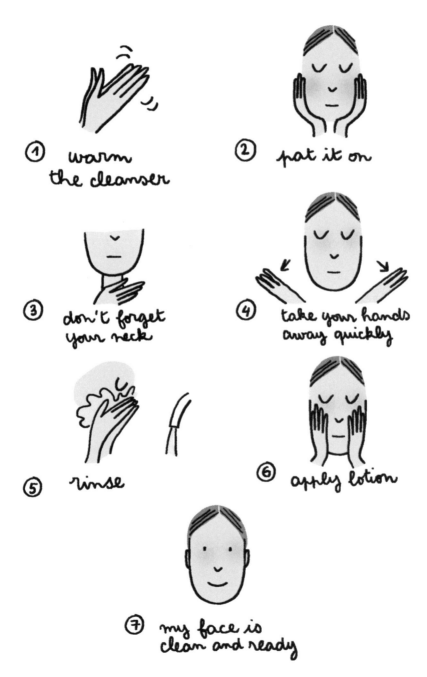

① warm the cleanser

② pat it on

③ don't forget your neck

④ take your hands away quickly

⑤ rinse

⑥ apply lotion

⑦ my face is clean and ready

Morning rescue treatment

One look in the mirror and... disaster! My eyes are swollen, a wrinkle showed up on my cheek, my skin is tight and my complexion pale.
Here is a quick solution, 20 minutes on the stopwatch (breakfast included):

1 Take the eye contour gel that you put in the refrigerator the night before and apply a small amount to the contours of your eyes. Drink a glass of hot water.
No eye care product at hand? Use an ice cube wrapped in a thin fabric. Rub it on your upper and lower eyelids, and while you're at it, rub it on the rest of your face as well. 2 minutes
2 Apply a super hydrating mask to your face after cleansing. 1 minute
3 Open the window, close your eyes and breathe 3 times deeply.
1 minute

Do you have to suffer to be beautiful?
Absolutely not! What's bad for your health is bad for your complexion. The skin is a sensory organ: if treated gently and with care, it reacts beautifully. Pulling at it to clean it better is like starving yourself to lose weight; you're better off doing nothing.

Every morning, when you wake up, drink a large glass of warm water to gently wake up your body and set it in "start" mode. To facilitate the elimination of waste and to promote a glowing complexion, add a few drops of lemon juice, it's packed with antioxidants.

open the window and breath deeply

4 Prepare your breakfast and sit down calmly and eat it. 10 minutes
5 Gently remove the face mask. Sitting on the edge of the bathtub, rest your head in the palms of your hands, this helps reduce swollen eyelids. 2 minutes
6 Apply a tightening serum pressing with the palms of your hands from the center outwards so as to relax the features and prepare your skin for make-up. 1 minute
7 Apply a day cream. 1 minute
8 Apply light make-up. Lighter colours make you look younger and less marked. Brighten it all up with blush if necessary. 2 minutes

And now, you're ready to get dressed, preferably in bright colours to show off and flatter your figure.

Getting ready: say repeatedly to yourself: "I feel good, I'm pretty." Breathe deeply, and adopt good beauty posture: Imagine a silk thread pulling you backward, relax your shoulders, pull your stomach in... and you're ready to go!

breakfast

tightening serum

day cream

blush

Did you know?
Cells renew
themselves at night;
the peak time is
between 1 and
3 in the morning.

Did you know?
Alcohol and tobacco
dehydrate the skin
and cause premature
ageing.

If you have trouble
getting to sleep, rub
relaxing oil on the arch
of your foot.

Night rescue treatment

A last minute invitation? Why not, but how do I camouflage traces of end of the day fatigue?

Still at work: pull out your emergency make-up kit and find a light bright enough in which to adjust your make-up.

- Apply a few touches of concealer in "commas" on the inside corners of your eyes and tap gently.
- Hide irregularities (spots, pimples, blotches, etc.) by tapping them with concealer to camouflage them.
-Use powder to set it.
-Enhance with blush (or a hint of lipstick if you don't have any.)
-Apply your lipstick.

At home: take advantage of being there for a quick beauty treatment!
-Put lotion on your face.
-Apply a super moisturizing beauty mask.
-Apply make-up that makes you glow (concealer, a little bit of foundation, powder to set and blush to brighten the complexion).

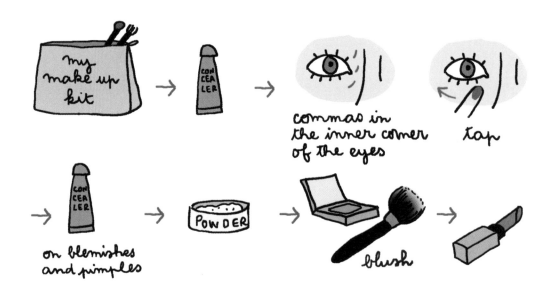

Night treatments: true or false?

You need a thick layer of cream.

False. The skin absorbs only what it needs. Remove the excess with a paper tissue or apply it to your hands and forearms.

You can use your day cream at night.

True, but best it's only to do so when you have to, it's always better to moisturize than not to. But night creams have benefits that day creams do not; they repair and nourish, and are usually richer. Take note: if your day cream has UV filters, you won't need them at night!

Night cream is not necessary for oily skin.

False. Oily skin has the same repair needs as other types of skin. Only the type of treatment needs to be adapted to meet the requirements of this type of skin. Use liquids or gels, which are lighter than creams or balms.
Only the texture of skin care cream must change to adapt to the requirements of this type of skin.

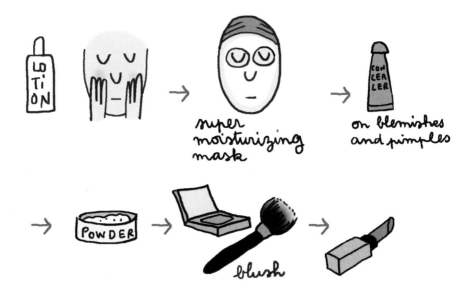

Beauty rules

1. NEVER push your skin around. Skin is like a rubber band; the more you pull at it the more it stretches… and that's when wrinkles settle in.

2 NEVER touch your face! That's easier to say than to do, because several times a day, without even noticing it, we put our hands to our face. But, if they're dirty, it weakens the skin and destabilizes its natural balance.

3 Always wash your hands before applying care products.

4 Apply products… with care!

5 Warm a small amount of each product in your hands before applying it. Using it at body temperature facilitates its ability to penetrate the skin.

6 Apply day or night cream by patting the whole surface of your hands on your face; move them from the center towards the ears, always gently preserving the shape of your face. Do the same thing with your forehead, the lower part of your face, and then the neck and chest. This light pressure with the palm of your hands helps the active ingredients to penetrate the skin without stretching it. Don't forget your neck when you use exfoliants or masks!

7 Cleanse morning and night.

Did you know?
- The production of sebum is greater during the day, it peaks between 12 and 3 p.m. Hence the importance of powdering after lunch!
- 30 degrees Celcius. That's your skin temperature. In some hot climates, your skin can be one degree warmer which can cause the skin to become fatty and subject to imperfections, pimples and blackheads.

I'm beautiful and I want to stay that way

Make-up: true or false?

Foundation damages skin.

False. Foundations are made of the same elements as skin care products. They are liquid and light and do not suffocate skin. Formulas have evolved, they have less pigment, are thinner and have lots of water for an immediate moisturizing effect. Foundations protect your face as they put an additional barrier between your skin and pollutants.

Lipstick is aggressive to lips.

False. Protecting, moisturizing, pleasant to use, lipsticks "coat" but don't stick. They "glide" without chafing. Smooth, supple, adherent, robust, they contain revolutionary formulas full of elements that treat your lips.

Powder dries skin.

False. Created from minerals and innocuous colours, powder, whether loose or pressed, softens, moisturizes and protects the skin from assaults from the environment while respecting its physiological make-up.

Mascara makes your eyelashes fall out.

False. The new generation of mascara envelops without smothering, strengthens, lengthens or even curls lashes. Rich in keratin, active ingredients that protect and hydrate and nourishing plant oils, they are good for lashes and sometimes even help them grow.

HELLO DOCTOR?

Why is it that when I'm tired my make-up fades faster?

faq ⑤ Being tired or stressed increases secretion of the sebaceous and sweat glands. Your skin is therefore oilier and "drinks" makeup. Remember to keep your skin matte.

What happens if I don't cleanse at night?

faq ⑥ The skin suffocates, it has trouble breathing, and impurities cause skin sensitivity, redness, irritation and pimples. To avoid damaging your skin, do not skip cleansing it at night. And if you do (accidentally) forget, exfoliate well in the morning when you get up.

Why do they call it beauty sleep?

faq ⑦ Because at night, the skin cells regenerate! Studies prove the multiplication of cells is at its peak at 1 am and at its lowest at 1 pm. Sleep well; it's important for your skin.

When my face acts up

★ I've got pimples

The important thing is not to stimulate the sebaceous glands, which are already over active. Get rid of all traces of impurities, morning and night, with a cleanser that fights blemishes.

Treat each pimple gently and directly without fiddling with it with your (probably dirty) fingers and without squeezing the skin. To absorb excess sebum, put a purifying mask on affected areas.

★ I have dull skin

Dull skin can be due to an overall state of fatigue. What you need to do is exfoliate more regularly. Do not hesitate to do so two to three times a week and moisturize well afterwards. Also, remember to oxygenate by communing with nature and getting some fresh air.

★ I wrinkle easily

Get in the habit of sleeping with your head raised. Apply smoothing products in the morning. Remember to relax as much as possible so your wrinkles can unwind.

A new wrinkle? Press on it for 10 seconds using the heel of your hand. If it's recent, it should disappear. And above all, moisturize your skin as much as possible.

★ I have tight skin

This feeling comes from a lack of lipids (your skin is dry) or water (your skin is dehydrated). Choose an appropriate cream, something highly nourishing, and apply it at least twice a day. In the evening, use it when you get home from work (on clean skin) and once again before bedtime. To enhance your cream, add 2 drops of nourishing oil.

★ I have red skin

Stress or weather conditions (wind, cold) can attack the skin. Maximize your skin protection by using a suitable moisturizer such as an especially thick balm in winter, for example.

★ I have blotchy skin

Your skin needs to be soothed and decongested. Use products that sooth and arm it against external aggressors with a protective cream for especially dry skin.

★ I have lines (especially in the morning)

Replenish your skin by applying a mask every morning for 5 days. And don't forget to apply your eye contour cream morning and night

★ My skin is rejecting everything

Your skin speaks for you: and what if, actually, it's you who is rejecting everything. Before considering changing all of your skin care products, relax as much as possible. Change your beauty routine by focusing on what makes you happy and minimizing the number of products you use. Your skin is lacking resistance for the time being, it's best not to ask too much of it.

spinach

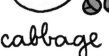

cabbage

oranges

tomatoes

HELLO DOCTOR?

Can I use my day cream at night?

faq **8** Occasionally yes, but not regularly as it is not designed to promote nocturnal cellular repair.

Can I use my anti-wrinkle cream on eye contours?

faq **9** No, you need a product carefully developed specifically for this fragile area.

Why is a balanced diet important for a glowing complexion?

faq **10** A glowing complexion is a sign of a healthy digestive system; the result of a proper diet. Eat a balanced diet and drink plenty of water and fresh fruit juices.

Can my face get thinner?

faq **11** Slightly modifying your food habits, eating healthier foods, will slim down the face first! Consider using draining massages as well.

My skin is drier since menopause, is that normal?

faq **12** Up to and during menopause, the youthfulness of the skin is put to a difficult test. Hormonal fluctuations increase signs of ageing: the skin is less elastic, it thins out, gets weaker, lines loosen up, wrinkles get deeper, not to mention the fact that collagen and elastin fibers become rare and less effective and sebaceous glands are stimulated less. It is therefore quite normal for skin to be less hydrated. Change your care treatment and choose rich products that reinforce skin fibers and make your skin feel comfortable, thanks to nourishing active ingredients.

And on your plate?

- Fruit and vegetables, rich in vitamin C which counteract photoageing: spinach, cabbage, oranges, tomatoes...
- Egg yolks, liver, butter for the vitamin A, an antioxidant, which preserves the skin's elasticity.
- Vegetable oils (olive, canola, wheat germ, sunflower, grape seed...) and oleaginous fruit (almonds, hazelnuts) for vitamin E, the "anti-ageing" vitamin par excellence.
- Egg yolks (again) and cold-water fish (salmon, tuna, herring, anchovies...) for vitamin D which boost skin quality and help foster a homogeneous complexion.
-Seafood and oysters for the zinc content and its anti-inflammatory and healing properties.
-Lentils, liver, black and white pudding for the iron which enhances tissue oxygenation.

egg yolks

liver

butter

oils

seafood

lentils

black and white pudding

TEST……… Age and you

How old is my skin(really)?

You're not growing older… you're getting better.
10 questions to evaluate your perception of age.

Contrary to what you think, we are 4 ages in 1!
- The legal age: the age on our ID.
- The psychological age: the age that we feel we are in our head.
- The social age: the age that people assign to us without really knowing us.
- The physiological age: the actual age of our arteries, organs and physiological functions.

Evaluate your perception of your age by ranking the 10 following statements on a scale of "never" to "always".

- People generally think that you look younger than your age.
  - ☐ **a** Never
  - ☐ **b** Rarely
  - ☐ **c** Sometimes
  - ☐ **d** Often
  - ☐ **e** Always

- You tend to have a look that is younger and more trendy than people your age.
  - ☐ **a** Never
  - ☐ **b** Rarely
  - ☐ **c** Sometimes
  - ☐ **d** Often
  - ☐ **e** Always

- You can easily climb three flights of stairs without getting out of breath.
  - ☐ **a** Never
  - ☐ **b** Rarely
  - ☐ **c** Sometimes
  - ☐ **d** Often
  - ☐ **e** Always

- When you pinch your skin, it returns to its initial position instantly.
  - ☐ **a** Never
  - ☐ **b** Rarely
  - ☐ **c** Sometimes
  - ☐ **d** Often
  - ☐ **e** Always

- You have forward-looking projects.
  - ☐ **a** Never
  - ☐ **b** Rarely
  - ☐ **c** Sometimes
  - ☐ **d** Often
  - ☐ **e** Always

- You exercise at least twice a week.
  - ☐ **a** Never
  - ☐ **b** Rarely
  - ☐ **c** Sometimes
  - ☐ **d** Often
  - ☐ **e** Always

- You're more comfortable with people younger than you are.
    - **a** Never
    - **b** Rarely
    - **c** Sometimes
    - **d** Often
    - **e** Always

- You feel younger than the age on your ID.
    - **a** Never
    - **b** Rarely
    - **c** Sometimes
    - **d** Often
    - **e** Always

- You feel that time is going by too quickly.
    - **a** Never
    - **b** Rarely
    - **c** Sometimes
    - **d** Often
    - **e** Always

- You still feel you want to accomplish a lot of things in your lifetime
    - **a** Never
    - **b** Rarely
    - **c** Sometimes
    - **d** Often
    - **e** Always

- **Note the number of responses for each: a, b, c, d, e.**
- **Multiply the number of responses by the following factors.**

    a by 0
    b by 1
    c by 2
    d by 3
    e by 4

- **Add up the results.**

Over 30 points:
You are on the whole younger than your social age. People often think you are younger than you are! Your head is filled with projects and you're looking into the future. Pace yourself and take a break now and then so you don't overdo it.

11-30 points:
Your social age generally corresponds to your physical and psychological age. People usually think you are the age you are and you're comfortable with that. Stay dynamic and enthusiastic about your new future projects using your maturity and life experiences to make them happen.

0-10 points:
You're more mature than your age. Maybe it's your personality, or your past experiences which make you take a step back and give you a sort of wisdom. To keep a dynamic internal force, be careful not to focus too much on the past.

HELLO DOCTOR?

Why does my cream flake sometimes?

faq ⓭ This is a sign that your skin needs to be exfoliated, or a result of too many layers of products or too much of one.

How do I apply cream to my neck?

faq ⓮ Get into the habit of applying your face cream "downwards" to the top of your chest and to apply your body or breast cream "upwards" to your chin. Both directions are beneficial provided you don't displace the skin tissue.

Why does my skin feel like it's tight?

faq ⓯ Because your skin is dehydrated! Drink a little every 10 minutes and limit your coffee and tea intake. Don't hesitate to reapply moisturizer during the day.

Can I apply a mask every day?

faq ⓰ Yes, if it's a cream mask that doesn't dry the skin out. Without replacing other treatments, masks increase resistance and smooth the skin.

Why do I still have pimples at 40?

faq ⓱ Because your skin is reacting to hormonal changes related to your menstrual cycle, but it is also sensitive to your stress level and your lifestyle (fatty foods, tobacco...). Take care of yourself and stay zen.

thank you for making
me so beautiful

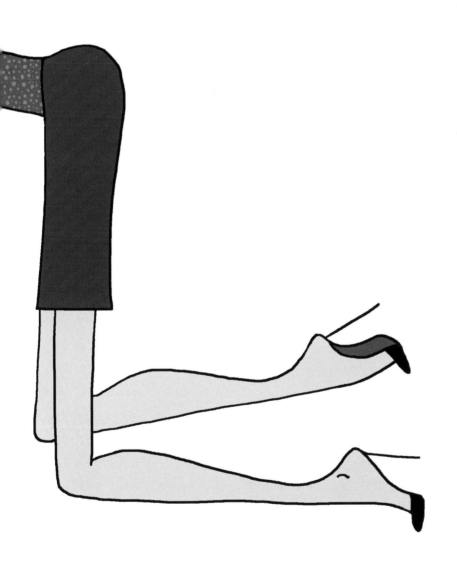

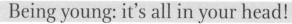

Being young: it's all in your head!

In addition to the "natural" beauty we are born with, some of our daily routines can have a direct impact on the state of our skin and the age our skin seems. Because, don't forget that being young in your head comes from a particular mindset: a mixture of being curious and contemporary, being up to date on all the news and trends, being connected and having a certain level of self-esteem. It's being content, knowing what's good for you, that makes you happy and understand your desires and choices.

Preventing that wrinkle from getting deeper. During your face care routine, press down on each side of the wrinkle with the tips of your index fingers several times in a row. This pressure technique will inflate the skin.

Adopt Rituals that keep you young, now!

- Get up before 9 a.m. every day, even on weekends! Make time to take time; it reinforces a sense of efficiency and well-being.
-Exercise (for real). We're talking about regularly and over the long term for at least 45 minutes a week, in all weather, without any excuses...
The secret? Find a sport that you really like, and that doesn't envolve certain constraints. Once you've decided what it is, put it in your weekly schedule.
-Work on your physical flexibility. A flexible body is the sign of a flexible, more open spirit.
-Cook for your body and brain. The best way? Vary the tastes and colours you put on your plate, it's best to build on diversity and balance.
- Make a note of each day. At the end of the day, take a moment to look back on it and note all the positive moments, mentally or in writing. Apply the happiness equation: 1 + 1 + 2 + 3 = 7 happy moments, on the whole a pretty good day!
-Get sunlight every day, summer and winter, to fight seasonal depression and fill up on vitamin D. Don't hesitate to roll up your sleeves when you're on a coffee break for example.

Something that's good for you

Empty your head at night by writing things down in a notebook or on a sheet of paper:
- thoughts that are weighing on your spirit so as to get them out.
- your to-do list for the next day... to get it off your mind!

And on your plate?

Focus on antioxidants, they help make skin look younger. They fight the free radicals, responsible for ageing, and improve the surface of the skin. The number one foods, all categories combined: garlic, almonds, eggplant, beets and broccoli. You can add variety with algae and green tea.

HELLO DOCTOR?

I have wrinkles like a barcode on my lips, what can I do?

faq (18) To improve the appearance of these wrinkles, exfoliate the area for 8 consecutive days and moisturize morning and night.

Why do some of my wrinkles make me look sad or tired?

faq (19) You can read a face like a book... Wrinkles, like handwriting, can say a lot about us. Upwards wrinkles are always more cheerful than downward wrinkles. Hence the need to live happily and laugh!

Why isn't my skin firm?

faq (20) Ageing causes a loss of skin tone. But other contributing factors such as pollution, sun or cigarette smoke, which further disrupt the production of collagen and elastin, responsible for skin firmness, can in turn be controlled.

Why does exposure to the sun increase spots?

faq (21) Overexposure favors the accumulation of melanin (responsible for tanning) and hyperpigmentation of certain areas (hands, necklines, face) causing spots. This phenomenon may be aggravated by certain medications and hormonal treatments.

My eyelids are sagging, what can I do?

faq (22) Chose an eye contour product with lifting agents and apply it morning and night.

I have a double chin, what can I do?

faq (23) If it's due to an accumulation of fat, change your eating habits. The double chin will go down right away. However, if it's sagging skin, use products with lifting agents to strengthen and improve the appearance of your chin.

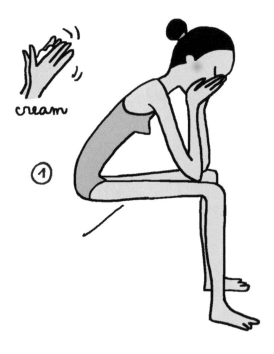

cream

Homemade face lift

You can perform a face "lift" at home with this method used in CLARINS beauty salons.

1 Warm a thin layer of your anti-wrinkle product in your hands then sit down, with your head down and your elbows on your knees and rest your head in your hands.
2 Slide your forehead down to the heels of your hands…
3 … then back down to your eye contours so they are completely covered. Leave your hands there for 10 seconds.
4 Move your hands to your cheeks. 10 seconds
5 Enclose your face with your hands, so the top of the wrists are joined at the chin. 10 seconds
6 Separate the wrists and now put your hands on your ears and press gently. 10 seconds
7 Take your hands and put them behind your neck to revive the circulation in the lymph nodes.

To slowdown the effects of ageing

Do's

- Sleep well! A good night of rejuvenating sleep makes you fresh and clear in the morning.
- Go to bed early once a week (around 10 p.m.): the hours of sleep before midnight are more rejuvenating than those after midnight.
- Eat light and avoid salt: a heavy and salty meal in the evening will causes your face and eye contours to swell when you wake up.
- Perform regular skin care treatments at home or get them at a salon.
- Be kind to your skin, do not stretch it or be aggressive.
- Look at the bright side of life!

Don'ts

- Avoid aggressive sun rays : they accelerate ageing. Be particularly careful when you are sitting on a terrace without sun block or when in a car behind the windshield or side windows because all UV rays are not blocked by the glass.
- Stop Pouting! Some repeated negative facial expressions induce unsightly wrinkles.
- Take a look at your lifestyle: stop smoking, don't drink too much, go out a little less and come home earlier...
- Avoid stressful situations whenever possible.

TEST......... Stress and you

Are you stressed out?

Evaluate your stress level by assigning values to the following 10 statements on a scale of "never" to "always. "

- You're constantly feeling overwhelmed.
  - ☐ **a** Never
  - ☐ **b** Rarely
  - ☐ **c** Sometimes
  - ☐ **d** Often
  - ☐ **e** Always

- You're anxious and worried about the future.
  - ☐ **a** Never
  - ☐ **b** Rarely
  - ☐ **c** Sometimes
  - ☐ **d** Often
  - ☐ **e** Always

- You're tired during the day.
  - ☐ **a** Never
  - ☐ **b** Rarely
  - ☐ **c** Sometimes
  - ☐ **d** Often
  - ☐ **e** Always

- You feel as though you're incapable of meeting all your obligations.
  - ☐ **a** Never
  - ☐ **b** Rarely
  - ☐ **c** Sometimes
  - ☐ **d** Often
  - ☐ **e** Always

- Your body is uptight or tense.
  - ☐ **a** Never
  - ☐ **b** Rarely
  - ☐ **c** Sometimes
  - ☐ **d** Often
  - ☐ **e** Always

- You have problems concentrating and have a short attention span.
  - ☐ **a** Never
  - ☐ **b** Rarely
  - ☐ **c** Sometimes
  - ☐ **d** Often
  - ☐ **e** Always

- You have trouble relaxing and letting go.
  - ☐ **a** Never
  - ☐ **b** Rarely
  - ☐ **c** Sometimes
  - ☐ **d** Often
  - ☐ **e** Always

- You're unable to bounce back or get a good night's sleep.
  - ☐ **a** Never
  - ☐ **b** Rarely
  - ☐ **c** Sometimes
  - ☐ **d** Often
  - ☐ **e** Always

- You're short tempered or annoyed.
  - ☐ **a** Never
  - ☐ **b** Rarely
  - ☐ **c** Sometimes
  - ☐ **d** Often
  - ☐ **e** Always

- You feel stressed.
  - ☐ **a** Never
  - ☐ **b** Rarely
  - ☐ **c** Sometimes
  - ☐ **d** Often
  - ☐ **e** Always

- Note the number of responses for each: a, b, c, d, e.
- Multiply the number of responses by the following factors

    a by 0
    b by 1
    c by 2
    d by 3
    e by 4

- Add up the results.

You have 0-10 points:
Excellent, you're not stressed!
You know how to handle pressure and manage it by taking a step back and letting go if need be. Keep it up. This is the best way to preserve your health and well-being.

You have 11 to 30 points:
You're showing signs of stress, which could, in the long run, have a negative impact on your health and your physical and psychological well-being. It is time to take the matter in hand and insert some effective stress-relieving exercises into your daily routine so that you can better manage the load and the pressure.

Over 30 points:
You are under a significant amount of stress. You must adopt some stress relieving methods and practices to better manage the pressure. You probably also need to reassess your objectives and respect your constraints in order to better balance your physical and psychological resources, on a daily basis.

I take a ten minute nap before a big meeting

Exercises that help

Breathing right
- Get comfortable, sitting or lying down in a quiet place.
- Concentrate on your breathing without changing anything. Just be conscious of how you inhale and exhale.
- Without forcing it, at your own pace, gradually increase how long you exhale by breathing through your nose if possible – slow and steady. Then inhale again naturally through your nose. This progressive increase in your expiration stimulates the parasympathetic nervous system (responsible for rest and recovery) which reduces the level of internal stress.
3 minutes, several times a day

Mental imagery
Our brain works through imagery and responds subconsciously to internal images. Top athletes use mental imagery to enhance their performance, prepare for competitions and help them achieve their dreams of reaching the podium.

There is nothing better for chasing away stress than bringing to mind images of a reassuring place for a few minutes. Imagine yourself in this place, real or imaginary, in complete security, without any pressure, or constraints. Visualizing this place will make it come to life: take in the colours, the smells, the people there, the serenity and calm that reign over the place.
With practice and meditation, you'll be able to recreate this feeling whenever you want to, through a simple mental image.

Managing stress
Daily stress increases the secretion of sebum, hence the appearance of blemishes when tension mounts! Relax as much as you possibly can by getting sleep, exercise and by breathing deeply and slowly whenever you feel the stress coming on.

You have beautiful eyes, you know...

During the day, your facial muscles contract with different facial expressions. Frowning repeatedly during the day can eventually settle in and foster the appearance of new wrinkles. "Eye relaxing" exercises will soothe out the lines and protect your face's youthful appearance.

Beauty routine for the eyes

- Treatment: twice a day, ideally in the morning and at night, put a small amount of care product on the tips of your finger and apply it with light pressure, without stretching the skin, starting from the inner corner of the eye and moving out towards the outer corner.

Be careful: classic creams (day and night) are not made for eye contours, which are different from the rest of the face and so do not have the same needs. With few sebaceous glands, you should avoid oily products on this delicate area, so be careful, you don't want to end up with puffy eyes!

-Removing make-up: for each eye, put make-up remover on a cotton pad, hold it on your eyelid for a few seconds (this helps remove make-up and avoids weakening the eyelashes) and then slide it delicately up and down on the upper eyelid, without moving the tissue. Get a new cotton pad and repeat this gesture: at the end of the make-up removal process, the cotton should come up clean.

Avoid expressions that 'mark' the eyes and their contours like: frowning, squinting (working too far from the computer or not wearing your glasses).

Beautiful, beautiful, beautiful... Once you're ready, dressed, made-up and ready to have a good day/evening give in to the call of the Smartphone selfie (taking a picture of yourself). It's a truly narcissistic act which builds morale. A beautiful smile (cheeeeeessse) and click, it's done. Be objective: you are more beautiful than you thought!

treatment   cleansing

★ I have dark circles

First identify what type of circles you're dealing with. Using your thumb, press on the inner corner of the eye contour where the circle is. If the area clears up when you remove your thumb... good news! You can reduce the circles. If nothing changes, and the circle is still there, they are most likely genetic and not a sign of fatigue.
In this case, it's easier to cover them up with concealer than to treat them. Do not accentuate them: avoid dark eye shadow (black, plum or grey).
To minimize dark circles, use a product that promotes microcirculation, and ideally place it in the refrigerator for a cold decongesting effect.

★ I have bags

Use a non-fatty, make-up remover, created especially for the fragile and the delicate skin of eye contours, without pulling on the skin so as to avoid aggravating any wrinkles.
Be careful: do not use oil based make-up remover on your eyes, or you'll find yourself, at the end of a few weeks, with puffy eyes.
To reduce the bags, rest your head in your hands with the heels of your hands over your eyes for a few minutes.

Something that's good for you

Relaxing your eyes... brightens your look.
1 To rest your eyes and facilitate blood circulation in the contours: close your eyes, place your index, middle and third finger on each eye, rub your fingers gently in circles in both directions.
2 Place the heels of your hands on your eyes for a few minutes, rotating them first in one direction then the other.
3 Put the tips of 3 fingers on your temples and massage in slow stress reducing circles.

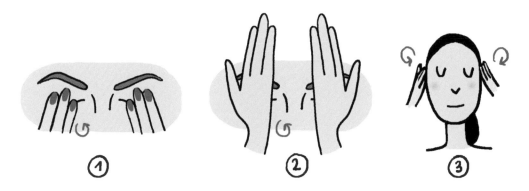

Teeth: getting them white!

-Enhance your toothpaste once a week with this age old recipe: Add a bit of baking soda to your brush of regular toothpaste, once a week.
-Drink... whitener! Prepare a cocktail of water with lemon juice – an astringent and whitener. Drink this daily, preferably in the morning and on an empty stomach.
-A clever make-up job! Choose a golden foundation instead of a pinky beige one to play the skin against the teeth. Avoid blue tinted lipstick, which make teeth look less white.
-Go electric: the electric toothbrush has a rotation power higher than you can achieve manually and makes your teeth whiter from the start.
-Finally, smiling is fine, but laughing is even better! It's been proven; laughter has a positive impact on your well-being as well as your physical and mental health.

A little laughing exercise

Sit comfortably. Place your hands on your stomach, the zone which centralizes the emotions, and remember something funny or an event that made you laugh. Make yourself laugh until you laugh out loud. If it doesn't seem natural at first, you'll see you'll get used to it very quickly!

Laughing and exercising, same system.

The hormones secreted by the nervous system whether in joy or while exercising are the same. So, whether alone, or with someone, force yourself to laugh a little to take advantage of its benefits. You can do this anywhere!

the city sun also burns...

Sun Attitude

The sun is the best morale booster there is! But it can damage the skin. Melanocytes are cells that produce melanin, which is both a solar filter (corresponding to an index 4) and an effective sun screen but not enough to protect you from over exposure. When the skin is exposed to the sun, it turns brown due to the increase of melanin: this tanning happens to protect the skin from burning.

Beauty tips

How to choose my sun product?
Take into account the elements of your 'environment' when out in the sun so as to better protect yourself:
-exposure conditions;
-the strength of the sun;
-duration of exposure;
-the areas of the body;
-the type of product.

Good to know: creams are better for the face, sticks are better for lips, nose and eye contours. Use lotions, gels and oils only on your body.

How to prolong my tan?
Add 2 drops of self-tanning lotion to your anti-wrinkle cream every 2/3 days until you get the desired effect. Also use an after-sun balm daily.
To make your tan glow, unify the color and even out the tan, exfoliate the dead skin cells twice a week.

The sun: friend or foe ?

 Friend:

- It helps us synthesize vitamin D.
- It thickens the epidermis making it more resistant.
- It gives you a beautiful complexion and puts you in a good mood!
- It helps fight seasonal depression.

 Foe:

- Extreme exposure, without prior adaptation of the skin, means a risk of sunburn which accelerates ageing.
- Over time exposure to UV rays alters the fibroblasts (which generate elastin and collagen, the fibers that keep the skin firm) thus accelerating ageing.

2

RAISE THE BREASTS AND STRENGTHEN THE ARMS

Bundled up under cashmere sweaters all winter, our breasts and arms re-take center stage at the first ray of sunshine.
Concealed or emphasized, our breasts are our 100% feminine asset. They illustrate clearly the fact that we are different and they can easily become an element of seduction, a way to attract attention irrespective of their size. All types for all tastes. What is certain is, the more you like and show off your bust, the more attention it will draw.

The problem with breasts? They are extremely fragile. They are held up by only one thing: the skin around them. Don't forget that breasts have no muscle tissue in them and are not firmly attached to the chest! Not only are they subject to the law of gravity, but also to various hormonal events (adolescence, pregnancy, menstruation, breastfeeding.) and abuse by inconsistent dietary practices. A breast's firmness is continually threatened and sags over time. This fragile and most feminine part of your body deserves a little attention. A rule: give your breasts as much attention as you do your face!

And arms? Usually forgotten until the unveiling... often catastrophic. Too big, too soft, they're ugly, and of course:

1 > you're exaggerating
2 > you're obsessing.

Before taking any radical steps such as making an appointment with the plastic surgeon, remember that unlike the breasts, the arms are mostly muscle. So, what difference does that make? Well, my dear! Muscles mean working out... In just a few weeks, with the right exercises you can get your arms back in line and the excess fat and sagging skin will disappear!

Daily chest and arm beauty routine

Daily:
Moisturize your breasts respecting the "natural bra".
Anticipate "clandestine" daily arm exercises to strengthen your arms and tone your breasts without even noticing them.

Once a week:
Exfoliate your chest with your body (or if you prefer, facial) exfoliating product to enhance skin elasticity. Be light handed on your chest and breasts, but when it comes to your arms, you can go full tilt on those stubborn areas like the elbows.

Beauty rules

1 Finish your shower by spraying cold water on your arms and breasts in a circular motion. Ideal for firming tissue and reviving the microcirculation.
2 Take daily care of your breasts and arms.

A bust in all its beauty

Breasts are made up of glands inside adipose tissue, which gives them their volume. They have no muscles other than the platysma, a superficial neck muscle. The aesthetic of the bust is due entirely to the nature of the famous "natural bra", a concept brought to light by Jacques Courtin, founder of Clarins. The shape, the curve and the position of the breasts depend exclusively on the tonicity of the triangle of skin that extends from the base of the breasts to the chin.

How to choose the right bra?

Lingerie, a second skin, should support without squeezing or leaving a mark. How do I know if the bra is right? The upper part of the chest should move very slightly so that the skin rubs against the fabric. Eventually, the chest will harden and become firmer and toned, better supporting the mammary glands that it holds and supports.
- Change your bra daily. With or without armature: vary your pleasures and keep the plunging necklines (which compress) for special occasions.
- As soon as a bra shows signs of weakness or an underwire is bothering you, throw it out straight away!
- Do not overuse the push-up effects of certain models: compressing the upper breast too often may atrophy the skin's thickness.

As for sports?

While exercising, moderately or intensely, you demand more of your bust. It is imperative to protect it with a special bra that secures it and limits the bouncing.

- Size: get the same one as you do for your regular lingerie but without stays or underwires.
- The type: preferably one with a Y or X in the back which holds the straps in place better, preventing them from slipping when you're working out.
- The fabric: choose one with good elasticity like spandex.

Did you know?
Breasts weigh between 10 1/2 to 35 oz (¾ of a pound to 2 ¼ pounds).

I'm standing up straight, as if a wire were pulling me skyward: chest up, shoulders relaxed. Keeping an eye on your posture at all times enhances your figure. Think of yourself as having the lead role in the movie that is your life and being under the watchful eyes of paparazzi, day and night, night and day…

For nice breasts and a nice bust

Do's

- Follow the outline and movement of the natural bra when applying products. For example, when you exfoliate, circle the right breast with the palm of the left hand from the outside in.
- Wear a bra the right size for your breasts. It should support your breasts, without compressing them. The test? It should never leave a mark, not even on the shoulders or the back.
- Exfoliate your bust regularly to improve skin tone. No need to press hard, exfoliation uses friction which oxygenates the skin, releases toxins and activates cell renewal.
- Choose your treatment as a function of your needs: a firming, form enhancing, tightening concentrate to lift your skin at the first sign of sagging; an anti-ageing product in the case of pigment issues, etc. Don't forget the toning effect of cold showers on your skin.

Don'ts

- To preserve the shape of your breasts, don't sleep on your stomach. The best position is on your back.
- Don't skip your bust when exfoliating on the pretext that the skin is much thinner than the rest of your body. On the contrary, it is better for it to exfoliate it.
- Don't soak for hours in a hot tub (it softens the tissue), don't overuse hot showers either. But better a shower than a bath, it's shorter.
- Stop the inconsistent dietary practices, stick with a healthy diet and way of life.
- Don't sunbathe topless: the sun weakens the skin that leads to sagging. Avoid exposure to the sun between 12 and 3 p.m. Apply high protection factor sun block to the chest and breasts and reapply it frequently.

orts that are good
r your bust:
vimming
reaststroke,
ackstroke), posture
ased activities
oga, Pilates)
nd dance.

orts to avoid:
activities requiring
equent and powerful
mps and bumps
erobics, horseback
ling, jogging, etc.)

Exercises that are good for you

You don't have the time or the desire to work out – your new beauty religion? To keep your bust in shape you need to build up your natural bra.

Stand up straight:
your chest is held up by your back

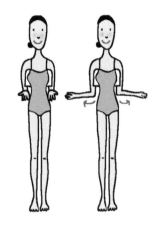

Start position: elbows tight to your sides, squeeze a book under each armpit, holding your forearms out horizontally with your palms up.
The exercise: move your forearms outwards holding your upper arms tight to your body. Hold for 10 seconds to work the back muscles. Repeat this at least 10 times in a row!

Smile

Force yourself to smile until you wince. This exaggerated expression contracts the platysma muscle of the neck and strengthens the skin tissue that support the breasts. Repeat this 15 times in a row. If you do this regularly, you will eventually see the tips of your breasts rise with each contraction. Yes, yes, it is possible with practice!

Pray

Put the palms of your hands together at nose level with your elbows horizontal, clap the heels of your hands keeping the fingers of both hands together. Do this 10 times in a row.
You can combine this with the exercise above.

yes, I know, they're magnificent

When my chest & bust act up

★ My chest has wrinkles

With age, they tend to wrinkle and mark more easily, especially in the morning. Looking in the mirror, you may get surprised by one or several unsightly wrinkles. Overexposure to the sun without any protection, when on cafe terraces in the city for example, will do it. The skin there gets thinner and less elastic.

Prevention: use a 'neck and chest' care product daily starting when you're young to maintain and restore this area's moisture to keep it firm as long as possible. From the age of 40, use a specialized tightening, anti-wrinkle, firming product for an immediate smoothing effect.

Use a 'sun' ritual at the first sight of rays. Carry high protection factor sun block in your bag, cover exposed areas like arms, face and chest. Don't forget the back of your neck if you have your hair short or up.

Repair: exfoliate your skin regularly, at least once a week, to increase its resistance and to encourage cellular regeneration. Moisturize every day before applying your make-up!

On your plate? Focus on Omega 3, excellent for the skin, cardiovascular system and blood circulation with fatty fish, linseed oil or nuts for example.

Get rid of negative energy

Putting your arms up to your elbows under cold water revitalizes the body and gets rid of "negative energy". This technique is widely used by beauty and health care professionals.

★ My breasts are sagging

Time and pregnancies, with or without breastfeeding, will change the shape of your breasts. A catastrophe? Not really. The good news is that you can reshape your breasts with a few appropriate actions.

Apply daily: "special breast care" products to improve skin quality, making it smoother and softer. Skin becomes more beautiful when it is touched and stimulated.

Straighten up! A straight back and relaxed shoulders flatter your breasts.

Exercise them! The specific exercises on the previous page will help them get their tone back and keep it!

★ My breasts are too small / too heavy

Too small: massage them daily, and spray jets of cold water on them in the shower, your breasts will be rounder and firmer and seem larger. A few kilos more and you may even go up a bra size!

Too heavy: this may be related to being overweight which can be fixed through a better diet and exercise (with the right bra!). If you are thin with large breasts, choose your bra well, one that is appropriate for the size and holds up the volume and is comfortable at the same time.

The right steps to a dream cleavage

This method stimulates drainage and preserves a youthful looking neck and breasts.
Warm your care product in your hands and apply it to your neck and chest.
Put your right hand on the left side of your neck, with your fingers under your ear,
and while applying pressure, drag your hand down to the top of your breasts.
Do the same thing on the right side with your left hand.

nwind.
e shoulders
ccumulate the
eatest part of the
ay's stress. Try to
member to relax
ur shoulders as
ten as possible
uring the day.
you can, put a bar
(between two
alls of a corridor
r example) so you
n hang from it to
ease some tension.

Exercises to keeps my arms beautiful!

We agree, beautiful muscles are an attribute of the male sex, and we're not
encouraging you to try for the next Ms Olympia title. However, keeping your arms
fit, your shoulders in shape and your skin tight is important. The way to do it
without succumbing to the scalpel of a cosmetic surgeon is: exercise, exercise and
more exercise!

Fight off fat

Good sports for the arms: any that strengthen the triceps as larger muscles tighten
the skin. Tennis, squash, swimming, rowing, boxing and exercises in a gym with
a coach. But also activities that work the back of the shoulders and the arms: the
backstroke, gymnastics and ballet.
Good exercises for your arms: good news, just 5 minutes a day doing one or more
exercises and you will get visible results within a few weeks.

Girlie push-ups to shape the arms

• Sit down on your buttocks: legs bent, arms bent and on the ground behind you, raise and lower your hips.
Do 3 sets of 10.

• Stand facing a wall with your arms out. Press your hands against the wall without raising your shoulders. Do 10 push-ups tightening your buttocks and contracting your abs without pushing on your kidneys.
To increase the level of difficulty move your legs back (but keep your back straight).

• Half push-ups: get on your knees and put your hands down in front of you, shoulder width apart. Bend your arms bringing your head towards the ground and then push back up.
Do this 5 to 10 times, then repeat.

Battling batwings...

This is a rather visual name used to describe the underside of the arm that has a tendency to hang down. It's usually due either to ageing or significant weight loss.

1. *Mini-Windmills*
Hold a small bottle of water in each hand.
Raise your arms to shoulder height so they are horizontal to the ground.
Make small forward circles and when your muscles are tired switch directions.
Do several sets of 10 circles.

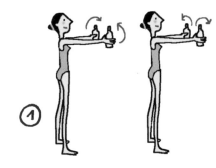

2. *Back flexes*

Still holding the water bottles, raise your hands straight above your shoulders. Bend your elbows so that each bottle touches your shoulder blades. Do this 10 times in a row. Take a break and repeat.

3. *Lateral flexes*

One arm at a time, still holding the water bottle, raise your hand towards the ceiling, leave the other hand down next to your body. Bring the arm down so that the bottle is just over the shoulder without touching it, keeping your upper arm horizontal. Do this several times until you feel the muscle warming up. Switch arms.

4. *Wrist against wrist*

Arms in front of you (you can do this anywhere, on the bus or even in bed), put the inside of one wrist on top of the other. Push the bottom wrist against the top wrist which resists. Switch positions.

And what about my hands?

Hands have a strong tendency to dry out because the palm has no sebaceous glands! The skin is thinner there than on the face and contains 4 to 5 times less fat. Therefore it is imperative not to forget them.

The absolute minimum? Moisturize every day, even without a special cream. You can use the leftovers from your day or night cream so as not to waste it. It's better if you use a cream that isn't greasy or sticky to the touch. It should penetrate quickly like an invisible beauty glove. Take this opportunity to stretch your fingers, one by one. Remember to exfoliate your hands 1 or 2 times a week. Massage your cuticles and nails with an oil treatment and treat yourself to a thick mask for 5 or 10 minutes! Beware of enemy no. 1 for the hands: age spots. To avoid this curse, don't forget to protect your hands from the sun, from April to October in sunny regions and from May to September everywhere else. Once the spots have appeared, the treatment (laser sessions) to reduce them is long…

HELLO DOCTOR?

Can I use an anti-cellulite product on my arms?

faq **24** Yes, if your arms have a dimpled cellulite look (which can happen). If your arms are fat choose a slimming cream, and if your arms are flabby, a firming product. The important thing is to use them regularly and in combination with other routines: regular exercise and a healthy and balanced diet.

Can I use my « hand » cream on my nails as well?

faq **25** Yes, and especially if it has a nail fortifying element. You can also enhance it with a nail contour oil.

Why do food supplements help nails and hair?

faq **26** Simply because they are rich in vitamin B, which acts on the quality of hair and nails. Do not hesitate to do a cure during the change of seasons.

Which exfoliant should I use on my breasts, the one for my face or the one for my body?

faq **27** The one for your body is exactly what you need for your breasts. Apply it lightly just enough to get rid of the dead cells on the surface of the skin. It is the best firming skin care product to make them smooth and gentle to the touch.

Do I need to protect my skin from UV rays when I am in the car or in the office?

faq **28** Yes, hands that are frequently exposed to the sun can, in the long run, develop brown spots. Use a "hand" cream with SPF or apply sun tan lotion after your cream.

If I don't wear a bra will my breasts sag?

faq **29** If they are not too heavy and your posture is good, you are working the triangle of skin between the chest and the chin. In fact, it's a good thing because this will improve and reinforce the quality of the skin. However, if your breasts are heavy, it's better to hold them up with a good bra, one that does not compress the upper part of the breasts.

How do I learn to appreciate my small breasts?

faq **30** By telling yourself that they will stay firm better than big breasts and that they could change and even get bigger during pregnancies...

3
A FLAT STOMACH, A SMALL WAIST AND A GREAT BOTTOM

S tomach, waist, bottom... All the curves that give you your feminine allure are here in this key section of your body.

Big or small, like it or not, these are the elements that determine your figure. And more often than not, we want to reshape them so that they correspond better to our expectations.

More malleable than other parts of our body, the stomach, buttocks and hips can, with the right exercises and diet, be altered. On condition, once again, that the routine is done on a regular basis and you listen to your body.

My stomach, my second brain

Contemplating your navel can be beneficial to the body. Look... or more accurately listen: the stomach does actually communicate!

During a first date, you feel butterflies fluttering in your stomach. The night before you go back to work, you have a stomach ache... as though your stomach was expressing your state of mind.
This part of the body is indeed a direct link to our emotions (conscious or subconscious) and our level of stress. Highly intuitive and receptive, the stomach is sensitive and behaves differently depending on our mood and our state of mind. If, for example, you feel like you just can't take any more, your digestion will go off and the elimination of toxins slowed. Quite simply, the stomach senses everything and "digests" more or less well the elements of our lives. Like with food, the stomach assimilates and excretes emotions.

The stomach is the center for our emotions and our vital energy. What modern medicine has recently uncovered, the ancient Taoist and Indians have been aware of for ages. The stomach, considered the seat of the soul, truly is a "second brain"; it has about **100 million neurons and neurotransmitters.** The two brains interact autonomously: the digestive system communicates with the brain through the vagus nerve which tells the brain what is happening in the intestines and gives orders to the intestinal muscles.

Another essential fact: the stomach produces 90% of the serotonin in our body. This biological substance is involved in the regulation of several essential functions: mood, satiety, libido, pain thresholds and sleep regulation. This shows you how listening to your body and stomach is an excellent habit to adopt so as to live a balanced and serene life. However, in Western societies, we are more on a quest for a flat stomach than a zen stomach!

It is therefore essential to learn to love your stomach, to accept it, understand its language and communicate with it through massage and touch. This will help free your spirit and increase your energy.

Put on your favorite tunes and apply your care products to the beat of the music! It's the best way to pamper yourself and raise your energy level.

Beauty routine for your stomach

As often as possible:

Use the Clarins® energy Wheel!
Inspired by beauty routines developed in skin spas, this method detoxifies the stomach and helps you find harmony through balancing out different types of energy while relieving stomach aches by learning to let go. Not to mention the draining and anti-cellulite effects it also has!

• While lying in bed, before going to sleep, breathe in and out several times normally.

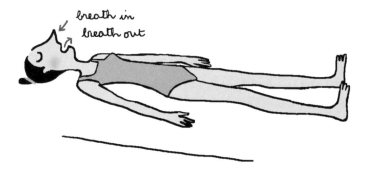

• With your hands flat on your stomach, rub your stomach gently in a circle clockwise, 7 times in a row.

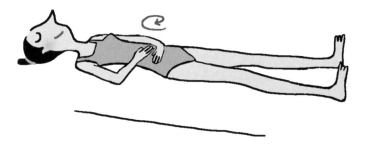

• Then slide the palms of your hands, one hand at a time, alternating them, from the tip of the sternum to the navel, then from the left side to the navel, then from below the navel upwards to the navel and finally from the right side to the navel, always in a clockwise direction.

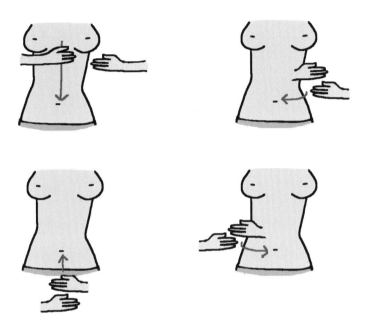

• Then starting at the tip of the sternum, using three fingers, make small circles pressing gently. Count to 5.
Repeat this a little lower staying on the line of the abdomen. Continue these circles all the way down to your navel.

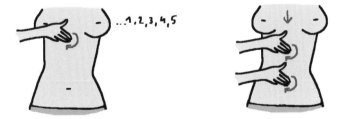

Free yourself from time to time!
Set aside blocks of time just for yourself. Go out with friends; go to a restaurant, the theatre... Or, if you're more of a loner, make an appointment at a skin spa, and treat yourself to a massage. The idea is to take time for yourself so you can unwind. Without any constraints or stress, your stomach will feel much better!

Several times a week:

Work out your perineum!
It comes up mostly when talking about
pregnancy and childbirth; but the perineum is
important throughout a woman's life. This
hammock shaped group of muscles and
ligaments that run from the pubis to the coccyx,
supports all the organs above it. The perineum
does have an important role in childbirth but it
is also important in our daily lives (urinary and
anal control) and our intimate ones (quality of
intercourse).

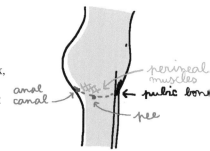

A chair exercise

Sit with your knees slightly apart, hands resting on the insides of your knees.
Contract your perineum and try and squeeze your knees together as you exhale.
Push back with your hands. Release gently.

Now place your hands on the outside
of your knees, and push outwards against
your hands as they create resistance.

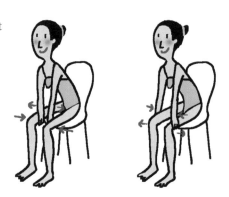

A bath exercise

While sitting in the tub, with
your legs bent push your knees
against the sides of the bath.
Then contract the perineum
by trying to squeeze your knees
together using your hands as
resistance.

From time to time or once a year:

Schedule a firming or slimming
treatment at a spa; try for 8 to 10 sessions
focused on the stomach.

Beauty rules

1. Tighten your abs (pull in your stomach) whenever you can.
2. Massage your stomach every day, morning and/or night, with or without cream.

Morning massage to really wake you up

After your shower, while you are applying your moisturizer, firming or slimming product, massage your stomach in a circular motion, first with flat hands then with your hands in a fist. Then finish by rubbing your stomach vigorously with flat hands to get the surface circulation going.

Night massage to help you sleep well

While lying in your bed, before going to sleep, breathe in and out several times normally. Rub your stomach in a clockwise circle several times in a row. Then, with your hands flat, slide them down from the sternum to your navel, as though you were pushing out bad energy.

good breakfast
A glass of hot water
freshly squeezed
lemon juice or
grapefruit juice
Tea
Whole grain cereal
with dried fruit, or red
berries, whole wheat
bread or a blend
(easier to digest than
white bread)

good dinner
Cooked seasonal
vegetables, vegetable
soup in winter
Fish (white,
salmon...), as good
as a diet pill
Fromage blanc
Valerian or passion
flower tea

Breathing through the stomach is good for your health!

Breathing is vital, and breathing can also help you fight the negative effects of stress on your body. So, to avoid your stomach and shoulders getting tight, adopt a stomach breathing ritual, and breath like babies do: first fill the bottom of your stomach with air then the top. This may seem unnatural at first, but once you feel its effects you'll be hooked!

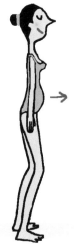

To unwind and strengthen your muscles effortlessly, inhale and exhale deeply with legs slightly bent. Expand your rib cage completely: even without breathing, the diaphragm will «lift» the stomach. By using the stomach muscles, you are massaging your organs.

This is excellent for your blood circulation, energy flow and for strengthening the abdominal muscles! Inhale, exhale and repeat 2 times.

A good exercise for flattening my stomach

While face down on the ground, put your weight on your forearms and your toes, raise your hips so your body is straight, hold this position for 10 seconds while tightening your buttocks and pulling in your stomach. Exhale while doing this. Repeat several times.

The right sport for flattening my stomach

Sign up for a Pilates classes, a discipline that works deep muscles and breathing; a gentle way to the perfect body.

Something special for each stomach

★ My stomach is big + my back is curved

An exercise for back pain: the pelvic lift
Lie down on your back, with your arms by your sides, bend your knees and put them hip width apart. Tighten your stomach muscles while flattening your back on the floor, then unroll your lower back from your waist to your coccyx. Do this about twenty times.

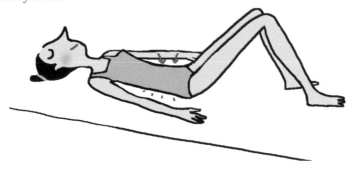

A slimming tip: drink plenty of water and eat fish, especially in the evening.

★ My stomach is bloated

To say goodbye to bloating
Chew! Do not forget that digestion starts in the mouth with saliva. Chewing allows the brain to analyze foods and prepare the digestive tract for the foods it is about to receive. When we chew well, the nutrients are absorbed better. Start by counting the number of times you chew before swallowing.
You will see that it is about 10 to 15 times. However, you should chew at least 20 to 25 times before swallowing. The advantage of chewing? You will be satisfied quicker, so you'll eat less!
Good to know: when you have a bloated or swollen stomach, avoid all foods that ferment: fatty cheese, fried foods, dried vegetables, soft drinks and alcohol!

I'm chewing, I'm chewing so I'm less chatty!

★ My stomach is round + my skin is loose

Your specialized cream: massage your stomach clockwise twice a day with a firming cream to facilitate digestion and excretion.

Your firmness ritual: finish your shower with circles of a jet of cold water in a clockwise direction.

Menu: all the fish and cooked vegetables you can eat. Taking just 3/4 of an inch to an inch off your stomach will tone your skin and make it look better.

good bye my stomach...

★ My stomach has stretch marks

Your beauty action: exfoliate, exfoliate and exfoliate some more to increase your skin's resistance, make it smoother and improve its appearance. They won't completely disappear (that's impossible) but you will, however, reduce them.

★ My stomach feels bloated

Your relaxation zone: you need to let out the emotions that are stuck in your stomach.
Express yourself through an artistic activity (painting, writing, etc.) or something else; the important thing is that it's released!
As soon as you get a chance, revitalize yourself by taking a walk outdoors. If you live in the city, make regular appointments at a spa.

Your healthy drink: drink a lot of herbal relaxing teas to lower your stress and bad energy levels to healthier ones for your body.

How should I dress to hide my stomach?

Do's

• With underwear that shapes or wraps. One with a cut that won't emphasize bulges.
• With light fabrics which give the illusion of a slimmer figure: Empire and trapeze dresses for you.
• With subdued colours (black, grey, beige, navy blue) ; you can also wear gay ones, the key is to have a unity.
• With a scarf tied around your waist, it will draw the attention away from it.

Don'ts

• Avoid: complex prints (polka dots, stripes, checkers, houndstooth).
• Frilly or ruffled tops.

HELLO DOCTOR?

I want to get rid of my tummy, is that possible?

faq ㉛ In addition to getting serious about working out (choose an activity that you like and that is not far from home or your office), you need to reconsider your eating habits. For example, avoid mistakes like: starch + cheese + chocolate (even dark!) at night. Remember you're going to bed afterwards, not burning it off. Opt for a light and healthy menu, all you can eat "fish + cooked vegetables". All washed down with good old fashioned herbal tea!

What are the best activities for maximum reduction?

faq ㉜ One of the most effective ones is jumping rope, an excellent cardiovascular exercise; 15 minutes of jumping rope is the equivalent of a 30 minute run. Jumping rope also improves balance and proper body positioning while toning the arms, shoulders, back and abs.

A small waist, that's for me!

It's difficult to talk about the stomach without mentioning the waist. This particularly feminine feature sculpts your figure and captures men's hearts. If you want to show off a small waist, you need to focus on strengthening your obliques!

Good exercises

Resisting

Lying on the ground with your left leg out and the right one bent, contract the perineum. Sit up, with your left hand push against the right knee while it pushes back. Hold this for 5 seconds. Switch sides.
Repeat 10 times.

Twisting

Sitting on the ground, with your back straight, legs slightly apart, arms joined in an arc above your head, rotate your chest from right to left as many times as you can.

Pedaling

Lying on your back with your arms folded behind your head and your legs slightly apart, lift your chest and legs and pedal without putting your feet on the floor. With each movement, turn your chest so that the left knee touches the right elbow and then the right knee the left elbow.

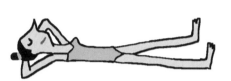 

facilitate digestion
…en applying
…ur daily treatment
…oduct, use clockwise
…ovements to
…cilitate digestion
…d excretion. Try it,
…e effects are almost
…mediate if you do it
…the morning before
…ting.

The best exercise: the Hula Hoop!

This is by far the most fun and the simplest exercise for trimming the waist. In twirling the hoop around your body, you are using all your abs and glutes!

and this is
∠ how to make
them all crazy
for me ...

And on your plate?

Favour fibers (fruit, vegetables, cereals) to facilitate digestion and lighten the stomach and the waist. Avoid particularly sweet or particularly greasy foods. Drink plenty of green tea which drains and avoid soft drinks.

Belts and things
To draw attention to your figure, do not hesitate to wear things that are tight at the waist or to accessorize your tops with belts pulled tight.

I like to drink iced green tea on the terrace

Dream hips

Women are not always happy with their hips!
Often regarded as too big, these joints, located between the thighs and pelvis, play an important role in a woman's life but can also quickly become her worst nightmare!

The hips' worst enemy: love handles. A very lovely name for a bunch of fat located directly on the hips that we pray will disappear!

Good exercises

Let's start with some good news: when you exercise the hips, you also work on your buttocks because you use your gluteus minimus and medius muscles!

Lying on your side, with your legs on the ground and slightly bent, raise the top leg with your foot pointing downwards, then bring it back down. Exhale with each movement. Do this 15 times before changing sides.
If you're feeling courageous, you can put weights around your ankles.

On all fours: arms and back straight. Raise one of your legs to the side at a right angle to the floor without moving the opposite hip. Exhale with each movement. Do this 10 times before changing sides.

And to lose those hips

On all fours, arms straight, lift one leg to the side at a 90° angle, knee bent without moving your pelvis. Hold this position for 3 seconds and go back to the starting position. Do sets of 10 lifts on both sides.

 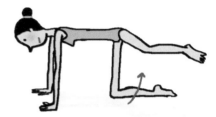

The right sports

To shape your hips, choose a cardiovascular activity which focuses on the lower body.
The top 3: zumba, salsa and belly dancing.
Not to mention the crawl; great for strengthening the stomach muscles and shaping the hips.

How should I dress if I'm hippy?

Do's

• In outfits that lengthen your body.
• In tops that draw attention to the neckline, either by their shape or colour. You can cheat with jewelry.
• Wearing the right length, not too long (this shortens the body) or too short (this accentuates the hips).
• In flowing fabrics of subdued colours.
• In skirts and straight trousers.
• In fitted Jackets.

Don'ts

Avoid:
• Big belts.
• Tight tops.
• Big skirts (Bohemian, or too jazzy).

A beautiful bottom

Too flat, too big, too round... women and their bottom, it's a classic love hate relationship.

In anticipation of potential pregnancies, the buttocks have extremely elastic skin tissues and highly active fat cells. Net result: high risk of getting plump and covered in cellulite.

Luckily, the buttocks are made up of not only fat but also muscles:
- **gluteus maximus,** located at the rear of the pelvis. It forms the curve (or not) of the buttocks.
- **gluteus medius,** located on the outer surface of the pelvis, it forms the curve of this part of the body.
- **gluteus minimus,** located under the gluteus medius, it is the smallest and deepest of muscles, and is responsible for the gentle curve (or not) of the buttocks.

Translation: yes, you can sculpt it without having to go through plastic surgery! And the buttocks' worst enemy is being sedentary. And if you consider yourself an active woman, with a routine of going from your desk to your car... Oh dear, oh dear, oh dear... And what if you add to this being the queen of inconsistent diets... Don't be surprised if your body, preparing for shortages from your next diet, begins to stock up and particularly in your bottom!

Beauty routine for your buttocks

As often as possible or, better yet, every day:
Finish your shower with a jet of cold water to strengthen tissue and fight cellulite.
Massage your buttocks every day, morning and/or night with or without cream.

Twice a week:
Exfoliate your buttocks at least twice a week to stimulate and smooth out the skin.

Beauty rules

1 While standing for long periods (in the subway or in line at the supermarket), tighten and release your glutes several times in a row to get a great bottom!
2 Don't neglect this often forgotten area: massage, exfoliate, moisturize...
Everything is good for them provided that the buttocks are soft in the end!

How do I cover my back-(side)?

The right sports

For the less sportive: take walks, for example after lunch, treat yourself to a twenty minutes walking break; this will help you to digest better. Remember to push down on your legs, lengthen your stride and tighten your buttocks. Plan a 45 minutes walk on the weekend for example. You can do this anywhere, in the city or the countryside; you just need a good pair of shoes.
Another good thing about walking? It enhances venous return and tones and slims the legs!

For the sportier types: dive into the pool with some flippers and do several laps kicking your legs. If you're afraid you'll get bored in the water, take some water aerobics classes!
Another option: all dance activities using the legs and the buttocks (rock, salsa, modern dance, etc.).

Good exercises

• Lying on your back on the ground, legs bent, lift your buttocks and back, to make a straight line putting your weight on your shoulders, arms and feet. Tighten your glutes as hard as you can. Hold 5 seconds and relax.
Do several sets of 15 reps.

Alternative: once the buttocks are raised, tighten your glutes and raise your buttocks even higher!

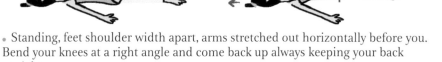

• Standing, feet shoulder width apart, arms stretched out horizontally before you. Bend your knees at a right angle and come back up always keeping your back straight.
10 times 3 reps.

Did you know?
High heels improve your figure. Being on high heels changes all the natural curves of your body, putting out your buttocks and your chest. If you want to really raise your buttocks, wear the stilettos instead of the 2 inch square heels!

• Standing on one leg, kick your foot backwards while tightening your buttocks without arching your back.
Do this 10 times before switching legs.

It's also time to take your bike out for a good spin: doing sprints and hills without stopping!

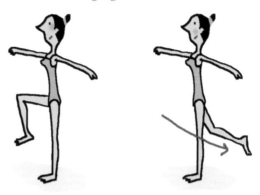

A good exercise for rounding out my buttocks

Lie down on one side, resting on your elbow and with your bottom leg bent. Raise the other leg without arching your back and do several series of 10 leg rotations (forwards and backwards) and 10 leg raises.

And let's not forget (even if you know):

- to take the stairs putting the whole foot down on the step so you use your heel to climb: this builds up your legs, abs and glutes.
- to avoid Escalators!
- to pick things up from the floor thinking about your back and building your glutes by bending your knees on the way down and pushing on your thighs to get up.

When I don't like my bottom

★ My bottom's too big!

Apply your slimming cream or oil in wide circular motions. Then use your fists, always from bottom to top, to tackle the area you want to change.

To stimulate blood circulation, continue the massage with your fists. Then every few seconds, open your hands and tap your bottom ten times. This helps blood circulation and promotes better cell oxygenation and venous return.

What do I wear to flatter my curves?

 Do's

- High cut trousers that give the buttocks a slight bounce.
- Pants with big pockets in the case of flat buttocks to give the impression of volume.
- Straight skirts rather than full ones if your buttocks are flabby.
- Draped dresses and empire waists which flatter all figures.
- To summarize, wear any clothes you are comfortable in, obviously, but not whose sole purpose is to camouflage your buttocks. Go more for clothes that accentuate your strengths. If you don't like your buttocks, then feature your cleavage!

Don'ts

- Low waist pants that flatten the buttocks and accentuate love handles.
- Pants that are too tight and bulge.
- Pants that are too wide and make you look fat.
- Fitted dresses or skirts if you don't like your figure.

HELLO DOCTOR?

I have a flabby bottom; what can I do?

faq ③③ First, start by exfoliating this part of the body several times per week to revitalize the skin. Finish your shower with a jet of cold water rotating the shower head in circles from bottom to top.

Spend 10 minutes every morning on "nice" exercises, you will see the difference within 3 weeks: use the stairs as often as you can and tighten your glutes between 20 and 30 times in a row; you will notice your buttocks getting bigger and shapelier. Between each series of contractions, relax completely so it doesn't hurt. The advantage of this exercise? You can do it anywhere: at home, in the office, on public transport...

Can I use the same cream on my hips, stomach and buttocks?

faq ③④ Yes, you can use the same cream for these three areas: either a classic moisturizer, or a slimming product. Whatever the cream, the important thing is the movement used when applying it. It needs to be one that promotes drainage and the decrease of fat cells. This is done in 3 steps.
1. Facilitating drainage by pushing a closed fist 3 times into the back of the knees and the groin.
2. Applying care products regularly using circular movements over the entire area.
3. Rubbing each area with a closed fist, always from the bottom to the top.

I only want to slim down below the waist, what do I do?

faq ③⑤ Massage the area that you want to see to slimmer every day and use your imagination like the top athletes do: visualize yourself as you want to be.
Make an appointment at a spa for a series of 10 slimming massages, you'll be amazed at the results. And to keep it all in place, take working out seriously, avoiding activities that are done standing up (jogging and step aerobics for example), which will add muscle mass.
The right idea? The pool, which very quickly, if you do it regularly, will give you back your figure!

If I apply my slimming product after having worked out, will I optimize its effectiveness?

faq ③⑥ Working out contributes to the elimination of toxins and the loss of salt, it helps to clean the pores and stimulates blood circulation... This is the first step in slimming that optimizes the effectiveness and penetration of your slimming product applied after showering.

I have stretch marks, what can I do?

faq ③⑦ If they are still pink, there's time to react, you can actually reduce them. To do this, there's no better solution than exfoliating 3 times a week followed by the application of a cream specifically designed for this issue.

Is cream more effective when it's applied with pleasure?

faq ③⑧ Our cells are more receptive to the active ingredients in a product when the effects of the texture and the comfort it provides are immediate. So enjoy this special moment.

Someone told me I have a gyneoid body type: what does that mean?

faq **39** This is a type of morphology. A woman with a gyneoid body type has a narrow chest, small waist, wide hips and sometimes, heavy legs. Gyneoid body types have a tendency to store fat in the lower body (hips, buttocks and thighs). Conversely, a woman with an android body type has square shoulders, hardly any waist, narrow hips and slender legs. This type tends to store fat in the upper body, primarily around the stomach. If you know your body type, you'll be better able to choose a form of physical activity that suits your needs.

I work out several times a week but I am not losing any weight, is that normal?

faq **40** Don't panic. You may have lost body fat and gained muscle mass! Muscles weigh more than fat. If you are looking to slim down your lower legs or hips, watch what you eat and avoid physical activities that are performed standing up so as to avoid building muscle mass. Any activity done lying down is recommended (not using your body weight will not incite increased muscle mass which is heavier than fat).

When I'm working out, do I need to concentrate on what I'm doing or can I think about other things to pass the time (like listening to music)?

faq **41** The important thing is to do it regularly and with ease. You can listen to music if that motivates you. Select a beat that fits your activity.

Are there different types of cellulite?

faq **42** Yes. New cellulite that is still soft is easy to eliminate. Cellulite accompanied by water retention makes the skin tissue look puffy. Fibrous cellulite, which is older, is painful to the touch.

What type of knickers should I wear ?

faq **43** The choice is vast and it is up to the individual to choose their "own style" according to their body type. Lace or cotton… the important thing is to avoid chaffing and that it is comfortable and is not too tight so as to leave marks and block blood circulation.

How do I learn to like my body?

faq **44** Change the vision that you have of yourself! Go shopping and buy yourself some dresses that flatter your natural curves and show you at your best. Don't forget that others see your whole self, whereas you are focusing on the parts!

What foods make my stomach swell?

faq **45** Broccoli, cauliflower, brussel sprouts. However, the digestive process in and of itself can create gas which causes bloating.

Do I have to suck my stomach in all day to have a flat tummy?

faq **46** Yes, you need to constantly be aware of your posture to assure a healthy body and its organs. Imagine that you're being pulled up towards the ceiling by a thread, lower your shoulders, straighten your lower back and suck in your stomach.

4
KILLER LEGS

Your legs: you want them thin, light, silky, slightly curved, but not too muscular...
A few tricks, well thought out exercises and a new daily beauty routine will **transform your legs into weapons of mass seduction**.
To give yourself a nice set of legs, we're going to focus on two high risk areas: **the ankles and the knees**. Because the worst enemy of a slim beautiful leg is a lumpy area that breaks the elegance of the lines, especially if your blood circulation is running slow.

Beauty routine for the legs

To get the visual harmony and shape of your legs that you desire, there is only one method, easy to apply: the self-massage.

As often as possible (every day):

Massage your ankles and knees to unclog the tissues. Rub your knees clockwise for better blood and lymphatic circulation.

For it to be more effective and more pleasant, use a dab of firming or slimming cream.

After this initial massage, use your closed fists on the areas you want thinner: the inside of the knee, above the knee...

Rub your ankles in circular motions, starting with the heel moving upwards towards the bottom of the calf.

Moisturize your legs and thighs to avoid dry skin.

Finish your shower with a jet of cold water to the front and back of the legs.

And then grow! Stand on your tip toes and hold that position a few seconds and relax.

Before going to sleep, raise your legs and shake them, turning your feet a few times. Apply a lotion specifically for tired legs. Alternatively, you can do this in the morning before putting your feet on the floor.

Every week:

Exfoliate your legs to get rid of dead skin cells and strengthen your skin's resistance. Focus on areas of cellulite and stretch marks. This also promotes a better absorption of slimming treatments in the future.

Whenever you can:

Walk with your feet in the water half way up your calf (or higher)...

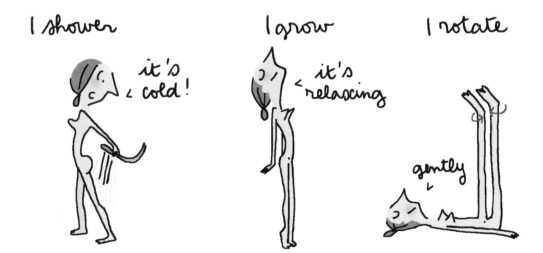

I shower — it's cold!

I grow — it's relaxing

I rotate — gently

Beauty rules

1 Put your legs up (to read, watch TV, sleep). This promotes circulation and gives you immediate results.
2 Avoid crossing your legs... Uh, yes, it is less sexy but crossing your legs slows down the blood circulation.

The beauty secret to thin, sculpted legs

Did you know?
By creating areas of shadow with a self-tanner, you can create an optical effect that slims the leg.

Every night for a month, after your shower, while the skin is still wet, apply to your legs an oil specially designed to reduce water retention. Wait a few minutes before drying your legs. You will improve their appearance and they will feel smoother and lighter.

Oh, what great legs!

Just because it's winter, doesn't mean that you should ignore your legs!
Moisturize, exfoliate and wax, all year-round, not just in the summer!

Pasty legs: sound familiar?

- You can improve them by concealing small defects, inconsistencies, veins, dyschromia patches... To do this, you can use your foundation for your face (there are also specific products for the body) or specialized and colored (yellow for the blue markings, green against redness) correctors.
- You can cheat with a self-tanning product. Gel or cream, it's pretty easy to create a nicely tanned leg. Once the skin is washed and exfoliated, apply a good amount of self-tanner, rubbing it upwards, avoiding rough areas (ankles, heels, knees...) so as to avoid streaks.
The secret? Take the time to avoid creating stripes.

Me and my legs, it's complicated

★ I have tired legs

The problem: inside the veins, there are valves that help the blood reach the heart. In some cases, particularly when it's hot, the veins expand and the valves don't work as well. Result: blood stays in the legs.

The right moves:
- Use a lot of cold water, going up the legs, in front and behind starting with the soles of the feet.
- Take showers, not baths.
- Wear compression stockings if your job requires you to be on your feet and whenever you fly.
- Walk often to boost blood flow.
- Swap your high heeled shoes for "rocker bottom shoes" with heels lower than the toes to promote venous return.

Things to change:
- Don't overuse heat (baths, sun exposure, hammams, saunas) which expand the veins and therefore aggravate circulatory problems.
- Avoid clothing that compresses the legs (slim cut for example).
- Don't stay seated long and often. You have no choice at the office? Stretch your legs often (and do exercises that you can do sitting down or take walks during breaks).
- Do not cross your legs.
- Being overweight aggravates tired legs.

★ I retain water

The problem: your lymphatic circulation is slow, causing water retention in the tissues. How to be sure? Lean your legs up against a cabinet for one minute; if it leaves a mark, you're retaining water. The solution? Manual or machine drainage in order to facilitate the evacuation of the water in the tissues.

The right tempo: the lymphatic circulation is very slow, you need to match your movements to this internal flow; take it slow and easy.

The right action: leg massages must be light. First enclose the ankle with your hands, then move them up along the calf and gradually to the knee and then up to the thigh. Once you've reached the top of the thigh, press your hands flat at the level of the groin where there is an important string of lymph nodes.

As for the cosmetics: choose oils that promote water reduction thanks to plant extracts such as juniper, for example, or a slimming draining leg product which acts on water retention.

And you're on your feet all day? Relax your legs often. Do toe lifts on a regular basis to reactivate the blood circulation, no one will notice.

As for the menu
If you suffer from tired legs, stay away from salt and processed foods, especially at night! Get into the habit of never salting your food.

Before slipping between the sheets, apply a draining body treatment (made from horse chestnuts for example). Don't forget that your blood and lymphatic circulations slow down while you sleep!

Did you know?
Fat cells, called adipocytes, can store fat up to fifty times their initial weight!

Why apply a slimming treatment twice a day?
Because massaging is as important as the quality of the care products. It's the virtuous cycle of beauty: the more you massage, the more receptive the skin is to the care products whose effectiveness is improved by massage... Result: toned and firm skin.

If you can, get a tennis ball and either standing or sitting, roll it under the arch of your foot. As soon as you get home, take your shoes off. If you have time, take a cool shower and then take a few minutes to relax with your legs up against a wall. At night, while you're sitting calmly on your sofa, trace a heart with your fingers into the center of your arch to restart the machine.

★ I have cellulite

The problem: you're obsessing on the lumpy appearance of your skin in certain areas of your body. These lumps collect on the buttocks, hips and thighs, stored there to be used in future pregnancies. Don't worry, it happens to all women. All you need to do is press the skin of a young slim girl without any apparent "cellulite"... and you'll see the lumps there as well.
Does that mean that there's nothing that can be done esthetically? That we just have to accept these dimples as inevitable? On the contrary! Visible cellulite is due to a basic lack of firmness.

Take the test!
At home, put your hands flat on your upper thighs, pull upwards. If the "cellulite" disappears, it is indeed the phenomenon which affects all women fat or thin as a result of relaxed skin tissue.
Cellulite amplified by a poor lifestyle (no exercise, a diet abundant in fat and sugar...) takes several forms. It can be:
• spongy, essentially due to fat;
• watery, linked to water retention;
• fibrous, often old and more painful, due to a hardening of collagen located between the cells.

The right strategy for fighting orange skin

- Eat better and healthier, avoiding sugars, bad fats and excess salt. For you it's as many fruits and vegetables as you can eat accompanied by meat or grilled fish. Use good oils (olive, canola...) and all foods and herbs that help digestion (pineapple, fennel, celery, artichoke, turmeric, ginger, basil...).
- Work out: choose endurance activities that promote venous return and muscle building in harmony with your body without "body building" which has no impact on cellulite: 45 minute walks, pilates, endurance training, hiking or biking, swimming for 30 minutes or other water sports (water aerobics or water biking).
- Massage yourself often! Unclog your ankles and knees first as they have a tendency to go into storage mode quite quickly, then do your thighs and buttocks to 'break up' the fat that has settled and to facilitate its elimination. On the difficult areas, use a specialized anti-cellulite firming treatment to firm up the skin and help eliminate the fat cells.
- After applying your product normally by smoothing and rubbing, you can also do a pumping massage in order to enhance the lymphatic circulation: with your hands flat on your ankles, press and release to 'pump out' the skin. Do this going up the leg.

★ I have legs like tree trunks

The problem: an accumulation of handicaps! Poor blood circulation coupled with slow lymphatic circulation and you are prone to water and/or fat retention. Result: your legs, which have a tendency to swell, no longer have any shape, hence the unflattering but graphic term 'legs like tree trunks'.

The draining smoothie
Using your blender mix:
¼ Pineapple,
150 g of grapes
(1/3 pound)
100 g of strawberries
(1/4 pound).

To avoid getting tree trunks

Do's

• Eat light in the evening.
• Walk as often as possible. On the beach, take long walks on the wet sand (excellent for venous return) or in water up to the middle of your calf or thigh (excellent for draining). Either way, don't forget sun protection and a hat!

Don'ts

• Lower your salt intake, even concealed, especially in the evening. It causes water retention in the tissues: if you eliminate it completely from your diet, you'll get quick results.
• Don't cross your legs: it blocks blood circulation and your legs swell.

And on your plate?

• Focus on foods rich in flavonoids that promote fluid blood circulation and tissue elasticity: grapes, kiwis, clementines and all red berries: raspberries, strawberries, blackcurrants, blueberries...
• Favor draining foods like pineapples, asparaguses, artichokes and radishes.
• Get your fill of antioxidants with garlic (the overall champion), almonds (which are excellente appetite suppressants), vegetables (broccoli, eggplant, beets...).
• Drink and overdose on green tea, the incredible slimming drink.

The right sleeping position

Do you want to wake up with a fresh complexion and light legs? Sleep in this position which enhances blood and lymphatic circulation: lie on your back with your legs slightly elevated (with cushions or books placed between the mattress and the box spring), ideally with your head on an anti-wrinkle pillow (Yes, yes, it exists!), especially if you have a tendency to find yourself on your stomach during the night.

Your legs and you...

1 Your skin is firm or very firm?
Press your hand flat on your thigh, move it from right to left. The more the skin follows the movement, the less firm it is.
Quick solution: exfoliate and take a cold shower every morning to get back on the road to firm skin.

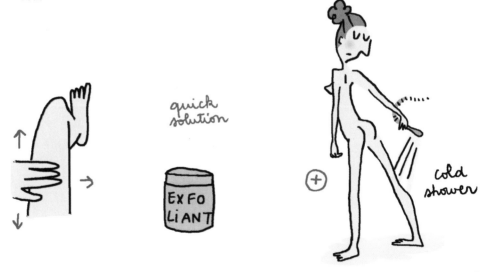

2 Is your blood circulation at its best?

While seated, press the palm of the hand, fingers outstretched, above your knee, for a few seconds. Remove your hand. Has the color of your skin changed? Can you see the outline of your fingers? Count how many seconds it takes for your skin to go back to its original color. The longer it takes the greater the circulation problem.
Quick solution: once a day, take your foot in your hands (thumbs by your toes). Drag your thumbs one after the other up the back of your feet starting between the toes, to revive the circulation.

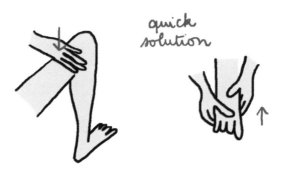

3 Are you (really) retaining water?

Press your thumb on your ankle or lower leg for 30 seconds. 1, 2, 3, 4... Remove your thumb. Is there a depression? Yikes, you are, without a doubt, retaining water; at the end of the day, your legs are swollen.
Quick solution: wrap both hands around your knee, squeeze gently, with your fingers behind the knee, tap lightly to promote drainage.

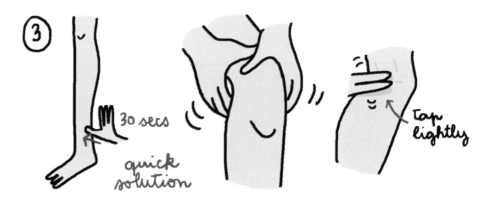

4 Can you fine tune your legs (or not)?

With your leg stretched out and relaxed, pinch the top part of your thigh and measure its thickness in number of fingers. Then with your leg stretched out and tense this time, foot flexed, measure the same place again.

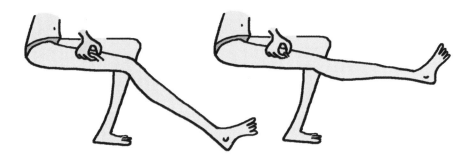

Results

In the first position, you measure the proportion of body fat to muscle mass. In the second position, your muscles are at work, so you're isolating the actual level of body fat. If you measured 3 fingers when your legs were tense, you can stand to lose up to 3 kilos (6 and a half pounds). Because the more body fat you have (calculated here in number of fingers, 1 finger = 1 kilo (2 pounds), the more your legs will show the effects of weight loss. Do this through changing your lifestyle: a better diet together with physical exercise.

Quick solution: press your fist into the sole of your foot three times in a row to revive the circulation. Then slide your fist up your leg from your ankle to your knee, first on the inside of your leg then on the outside. Continue up the thigh with both fists, one after the other, first on the top then on the inside and then on the outside of the thigh.

quick
solution

Ice cubes for light legs

In an ice cube tray kept in the freezer for just this purpose, prepare ready to use special tired legs ice cubes. Put a mixture of 50% water, 50% special heavy legs care product into the ice cube tray and then put it into the freezer. When you feel your legs tingling, especially at the end of the day or in very hot weather, rub one of your ice cubes on your ankles, calves and behind your knees to give a burst of cold thanks to the vasoconstriction it creates.

Drink and drain!

It's advisable to drink 1 ½ liters (34 oz) of water a day, preferably outside meal times, so as not to bloat the food you've eaten and slow digestion. Favour flat bottled water for its minerals and draining infusions such as red vine, dandelion or cherry stem. It's important to stimulate the venous return in legs that tend to swell as a result of water retention.

Another figure friendly drink is green tea. Here too, drink it outside of meal times and without milk. The secret of this drink, in use for thousands of years in Asia, lies in its high catechin content. These polyphenols, powerful antioxidants, play a role in the distribution of fat in the body and in weight control. In addition, its tannins limit the absorption of fat and its polyphenols promote sugar burning (and therefore neither of them is stored!). Hence its reputation as the slimming drink!

Something incredibly good for you

Whenever you get a chance, flex your toes to activate the blood circulation, rotate and stretch your ankles without lifting your heel from the ground. Along the same lines, tap your heels to reboot blood flow.

At the end of the day, once you've taken off your shoes, curl your toes as hard as you can for a few seconds, straighten them and then spread them.

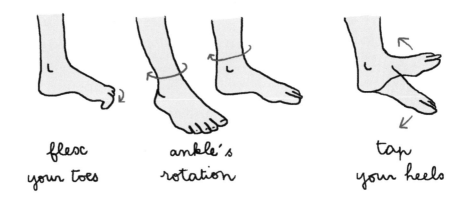

flesc
your toes

ankle's
rotation

tap
your heels

HELLO DOCTOR?

I have very dry skin on my legs, is it serious doctor?

faq **47** The skin on the legs has fewer sebaceous glands than the rest of the body. Friction from clothing and lack of hydration causes a snakeskin effect with some flakiness. Exfoliate thoroughly to remove dead cells then moisturize copiously to restore the skin's hydrolipidic layer.

For the first few days, apply your moisturizer in a thick layer like a mask, morning and night, to regulate the skin's hydration rate. Go with a highly moisturizing 'balm' and a lot of oil. Hurray for silky skin!

My knees are too big for my taste, what can I do?

faq **48** Every time you shower, exfoliate in a circular motion to boost blood circulation and optimize the efficiency of the rest of the treatment. After your shower, once your skin is dry, with your hand in a fist, apply a detox oil or cream in the event of excess fat.

I have legs that swell when it's hot and a puffy face in the morning, what can I do?

faq **49** The two phenomena are actually linked! If your legs tend to swell in the morning when you wake up after several hours spent lying down, there's a good chance that your face will as well. Sleep with your legs slightly elevated, you'll quickly see the difference.

Choose the right sport

All sports are beneficial provided, of course, you do them regularly, i.e. at least once a week. Target activities that work the lower limbs and facilitate venous return such as biking, water biking, fast or Nordic walking. Sports that build muscle slowly through long progressive movements are also good: swimming, yoga, stretching... However, if your legs are fragile and prone to spider veins and the sensation of heaviness, avoid all abrupt sports such as tennis, jogging and even mountain biking which is just a series of shocks.

Operation slim, shapely legs

Our advice: start with a short session, 5 to 10 minutes every morning or evening to cement this new lifestyle objective. Then increase the time of the session. And above all, vary the exercises so as not to get bored!

• Standing, legs straight, feet hip width apart, go up on your toes and then back to the starting position. Do this 20 times in a row.

• Standing, feet hip width apart, legs slightly bent, go up and down quickly as though you were trying to pick something up. Do this 20 times in a row.

When I don't like my legs

First and foremost, think positive! Focusing on one part of the body leads to a tendency to exaggerate its defects.

★ My thighs are too big

- The right sport: one swallow does not a summer make, exercise is good… but in moderation (not more than 45 minutes at a time)! Otherwise you may end up with even more muscular thighs!
  For you: swimming which shapes the body harmoniously, as do all water sports (water aerobics, water biking…).
- A good exercise: standing, legs straight, feet hip width apart, raise the left leg to the left, and back to the starting position, at least 15 times in a row and then switch legs.

- As for the cosmetics: apply slimming care products once or twice a day in an upward motion.

★ My thighs are too flabby

- The right sport: all activities which tone and round out the muscles without building them up too much. The best: jump rope or fitness exercises with a resistance band. More traditional but just as effective: Pilates or water aerobics.
- A good exercise: standing, feet slightly further than hip width apart, "squat": bend your knees with your arms stretched out in front of you, as though you were going to sit in a chair. Hold the sitting position for a few seconds and go back up. Start with 15 and increase the number each session.

Stay motivated:
when you feel a pain in your thighs, it means it's working!

- While lying down with your legs bent and hip width apart, raise and tighten your buttocks, while pushing the pelvis upwards. Hold this position a few seconds, bring it back down without putting your buttocks on the ground and repeat. Do this at least 20 times.

- While lying on your right side with your right leg extended for support, raise and lower your left leg slowly, foot reflexed, without it touching the ground. Do this at least 15 times before switching sides.

• While lying on your back, lift your legs and pedal forwards then backwards for at least 3 minutes.

• While standing, legs hip width apart, bend your legs, with your hands on your knees. Straighten your legs as you go up on your toes. The more your knees are bent the more difficult it is. Do this at least 10 times.

• Sit with your back against the wall or in a chair, put your hands and elbows on the inside of your knees. Inhale and exhale while squeezing your knees together for 10 seconds. Your muscles will contract. Do this 3 times in a row.

• As for the cosmetics: use a firming cream daily, and exfoliate your thighs two to three times a week mixing a bit of your tired leg treatment into your exfoliant. Rub your legs from the feet up focusing on the knees. It's refreshing and mega-toning.

Are you bath...

You know that baths are not that good for you, but never-the-less a life without baths is unthinkable. Here are a few tips to limit the damage to your skin.
- Try taking warm baths (37 °C), never hot ones.
- After you're finished with your bath, drain out the water and, sitting in the tub, run cold water on your legs from the toes up to your upper thighs focusing on your ankles and knees. If your tap allows it, alternate the intensity and don't forget the back of your legs.

... or shower?

Water at the right temperature (between 18 and 24 °C) is still the simplest and most effective way to facilitate circulation, prevent the varicose veins and firm up skin tissue. Yes, but what's the best way to do it?
Sit in your empty bathtub, legs straight, drain plugged: move the showerhead up your legs from the ankle to the thighs until your legs are completely wet.
Tip: start with warm water and progressively reduce the temperature.

The benefits of cold water:
- It relieves the sensation of tired legs by facilitating vasoconstriction.
- It enhances the effects of your slimming program (creams and food intake) by activating blood and lymphatic circulation.
- It helps firm up the skin.
- It encourages the body to... burn calories (from 120 to 150). Good tip: once out of the shower, don't dry yourself off right away so you can burn a few more calories!
- It makes your face look good and full of energy.
- It tightens the hair cuticles making the hair shinier.
- It expels negative energy.
- It fights stress: it's true, a jet of cold water on the thighs soothes anxiety.
- It helps fight insomnia – a foot bath up to mid-calf for a few minutes will lighten the spirit burdened by thoughts churning around in your head and help you sleep.

Yes, but it's too cold!

- Consider it a challenge!
- Congratulate yourself afterwards and why not treat yourself to a wellness or beauty reward.
- Do it (really) gradually. For example, start by filling a basin (or the bottom of the tub) with cold water and dip your feet and hands in... in order to get used to it slowly. Then the next day, "wet" your calves and your forearms. You will see that it's not as hard as all that, and you'll want to go further. If it's still too hard for you, use an ice cube to get used to it, rubbing it on your legs, the back of your knees, your groin, lower back, arms, face, neck...

Drinking water reduces the signs of stress

Drinking a glass of water after an emotional shock or a particularly stressful situation reduces the physical and psychological effects of this modern malady. Stress causes dehydration, and conversely, when the body lacks water, it presents the same symptoms as when it is under stress: increased hormone secretion, tension and heart rate.

So, before running a meeting, for example, don't hesitate to drink some water to reduce your stress level.

How should I dress: the proper dress code

Do's

- Choose smart outfits: tights and other slimming legwear! If your thighs are really big, invest in boxers.
- Don't forget that the shoe makes the leg, a heel can flatter or fatten a leg.
- Remember to always reveal your ankle: yes, that means low cut sneakers!
- Adapt your shoes to the shape of your legs: stilettos are perfect for thin legs, but avoid them with "tree trunks".
- Wear your skirts and dresses the right length to flatter your legs: just above the knee.
- Favor pants with a classic straight cut.

Don'ts

- Avoid high top sneakers that cut the leg off at the ankle.
- Stay away from wedges if you have thick legs.
- Forget slim cut or other tight fit pants.

I'm stressing I drink

Is it true that stress can cause cellulite?

faq **50** Too much stress, yes! If a fair dose of stress stimulates body functions, far too much stress or chronic stress becomes truly harmful: the adrenal glands release high amounts of cortisol, the stress hormone. This changes eating behavior, promotes fat storage and hampers proper elimination. 'Bad' stress causes swelling, blocking blood, lymph and energy circulation! Cortisol has different effects on weight gain: it sends powerful signals to the brain that increase our appetite and frequency of our cravings for comfort and pleasure foods (sugar, fats or alcohol) which are ruthless to our figures.

Spider veins, varicose veins what's the difference?

faq **51** Spider veins are unsightly tiny blood vessels one millimeter in diameter and visible to the naked eye. Varicose veins are bigger, just below the skin and can be painful. Make an appointment with a phlebologist for treatment.

Are blood circulation issues hereditary?

faq **52** In most cases, venous insufficiency is genetic, and can appear at any time. If you are aware of any cases in your family history, do not hesitate to consult a phlebologist as a preventive measure.

My skin is getting drier as I get older?

faq **53** As we get older, our body has a natural tendency to dry out faster than our face because the sebaceous glands, responsible for the secretion of the oily matter on the surface of the skin are less active. Hence the importance of applying a moisturizer daily that limits water evaporation and replenishes the skin's water reserves.

What's more effective: a massage or slimming cream?

faq **54** Everything passes through the bloodstream. To lose weight in a particular area, it is essential to massage it. The use of a slimming cream will enhances the effects of the massage.

Are there any nutritional supplements that I should take to help tired legs?

faq **55** For all of you who suffer from tired achy legs (sales people, air hostesses, nurses, etc.) before considering nutritional supplements, think about applying a specialized leg energizing care product to relax your legs, revitalize the blood circulation and relieve the discomfort associated with tired legs. For travelers, apply the product before departure (airplane flights or long car trips…). Sleep with your legs elevated so as to promote blood circulation and to assure your legs are fit in the morning.

5
AND MY FEET, DO YOU LIKE MY FEET?

They hold us up all-day long carrying our body weight. It all depends on them, our mobility, our well-being... and even our relaxed features! They play a key role in our equilibrium and stability. So much so that a small imbalance in our feet and our whole body is thrown off balance, with repercussions on the legs and even the back! The heel is the first part of the body to touch the ground when we walk, toes serve as stabilizers. Also, putting our feet on the floor when sitting or standing allows us to reconnect with the earth; to feel something solid, be in touch with reality, get a foothold and regain self-confidence.

The driest part of the body, feet are devoid of sebaceous and rich in sudoriparous glands (sweat glands). They also aren't spared the ravages of time: loss of elasticity, hardening of the balls of the feet, thickening of the nails...

Confined in shoes all winter, hidden from the eyes of others, they are rarely pampered except when the good weather arrives announcing the return of sandals. They are often forgotten in beauty rituals. Did you know that we take between 8 and 10 000 steps a day? That means that over a lifetime we'll have walked 4 times the circumference of the earth. Our feet deserve a little attention!

Taking care of our feet is the best thing we can do for ourselves. To be just right from head to toe is the ultimate sign of self-respect. Make yourself beautiful for yourself before making yourself beautiful for others.

The beauty routine for feet

A little attention every day prolongs the foot's youthfulness and well-being.

Every day:
-Finish your shower with a jet of cool water on your feet, tops and bottoms and your calves.
- Apply a cream, preferably one specifically designed for the feet (more emollient). Here also, tops, and bottoms focusing on the nails and heels, and avoid putting the cream between the toes. Apply using upward movements towards the ankle to stimulate the venous return.
-Take your shoes off when you get home from work. If possible, relax a few minutes, elevating the legs above the heart, against a wall for example.

Once a week:
- Cut the nails slightly rounded to avoid the famous ingrown toenail.
- Enjoy this relaxing ritual, inspired by the salons, that allows you to unwind while taking care of your feet.

very day,
edicate a little
me (less that
minutes!) to your
et, before going
o sleep for
xample:
, you'll feel
uch better;
, you'll enjoy
is mini relaxing
oment,
, rejuvenating
ctivity for your feet.

Sit comfortably on a chair or on the side of the tub. Soak your feet in a relaxing bath. While unwinding, drag your hands from your ankles to your calves, to sooth and revitalize your legs.
A foot bath has a relaxing effect and also allows you to soften dead skin.

minutes in a
oot bath at 37 °C
elieves pain related
o tired feet.
0 minutes in a
5 °C foot bath
timulates blood
irculation.

With the left ankle on the right knee, spread the exfoliant from the toes towards the heel on wet skin 5 times in a row. Switch feet.

Now, continue the ritual:

1 Rub circles at the base of the toes with your thumbs.
2 Take your foot in both hands and rub the top of the foot several times up and down from the toes to the ankle. Do the same thing on the bottom of the foot.
3 Rub a heart shape in the center of the soles of the foot with your two thumbs. Repeat this three times.
4 Press down on the center of the heart with the knuckle of your bent index finger. This relaxes the foot and activates blood circulation, targeting the "heart of the leg".
5 Place your thumbs on the ball of the foot, and rub your whole foot in small circular motions.
6 Join your hands around the ankle without squeezing. Rotate them upwards.

Use Nail polish remembering to protect the nail with a basecoat. Let the nails breathe a few days between applications.

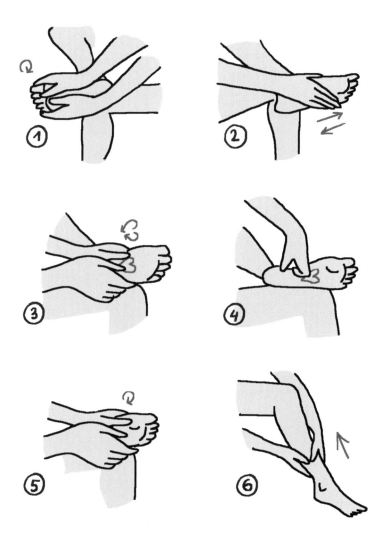

7 With thumb and forefinger pinch the hollow of the ankle then rub this area going up the leg.
8 Finish with a rotating motion with both hands going up the leg.

As soon as the need arises:
To smooth the lines and relax your feet, apply your regular foot product, take your foot in both hands, thumbs on the top of the foot, the fingers under the arch: "rub it", from the toes to the heel. You can do this several times in a row, the perfect thing to help you unwind. Don't forget that all the nerves and blood capillaries end in the arch of the foot.

Beauty tips

1 Spend a little time on your feet every day!
2 Wear different shoes every day (good news for shoes addicts!)
3 Take your shoes off when you get home.

File or not-to file?

This instrument is very abrasive and shouldn't be over used, especially considering that putting a new type of pressure on your foot could result in a new corn! Exactly what you don't want!

Sand, the natural exfoliant

In summer, when you're on the beach, walk in the wet sand, taking care to fully roll your foot with each step; first your heels, then the soles until they're flat, and finally the toes.
After this walk, excellent for revitalizing the body, sit on the water's edge and take advantage of nature's great natural exfoliant: sand. Take wet sand and rub it gently onto each foot focusing on the rough areas. Your feet will be all soft!

A good exercise
At the office
Sit all the way back in your chair so as to keep your back straight, relax your shoulders and place your feet flat on the floor; crossing your legs cuts off the blood circulation and blocks energy flow.

Best foot forward!
Relax your feet at the end of the day using a tennis ball: put the ball on the ground, put your foot on top of it and move it in small circles. Enjoy this short break at home or even at the office!

Keeping my feet soft and beautiful...

 Do's

• Buy your shoes at the end of the day, when your feet and legs have a tendency to be swollen to avoid having to squeeze into your new shoes.
• Make sure, when you get out of the shower, to dry well between your toes. Moisture is the foot's worst enemy!
• Use sunscreen to avoid sunburn and photoageing effects of the sun's rays. Remember your feet!

 Don'ts

• Don't overuse foot files or other pumice stones under the pretext of removing dead skin cells and corns.
• Don't forget your feet during the winter under the pretext that no one sees them! Or, take a week's holiday in the sun and show off your beautiful feet!
• Don't let the nail polish on your toes get worn. You deserve better than that!

Did you know?
The skin of your feet is 10 to 15 times thicker than it is anywhere else. Another good reason to exfoliate!

Wearing heels has affected my feet: what do I do?

faq **56** Respect both your shoes and the well-being of your feet by alternating flats and heels as often as you can.

My feet sweat, is it serious doctor?

faq **57** Feet have thousands of sweat glands. Stress can, effectively, make you sweat more. Wash your feet in the morning and at night, wear different shoes every day and avoid stockings and synthetic socks. Relax as often as possible to reduce stress!

My feet are very dry, doctor, what do I do?

faq **58** Apply cream every day especially to the heels. Once or twice a week apply a thick layer of your care product and put on a pair of cotton socks. Keep this 'mask' on overnight. When you wake up, you'll see the difference!

You could also add 2 drops of oil to your cream for a greater effect.

I'm exfoliating, I'm exfoliating, I'm...

6

CLARINS WORLDWIDE BLOG Q&A

Because **listening to all women** is one of our greatest desires, we asked journalists and bloggers around the world to send us all their beauty questions. The result is very moving because their questions addressed everything from makeup to beauty care including use of plants in cosmetics. Being able to providing answers to their questions seemed so important that **we decided to devote an entire chapter to advising them and you on how to always look your best!**

Facials

Day & night care

Should I use the same cream all year round, or change it monthly or with the seasons?
Select your cream according to your skin needs.
Up to the age of 30, you should be able to use the same products all year long, because your skin is less sensitive to the change in climate (except of course if you're heading for the North Pole!).
After 35, the skin is more sensitive to seasonal variations and changes more easily. Equalize your skin using different creams, light ones in summer and thicker ones in winter. Optimize the effects of your daily treatments by applying a mask one to seven times a week on perfectly cleansed skin: moisturizing, anti-ageing, energizing... the choice is vast!
From 45/50, the skin is even more sensitive so it reddens more easily. This new sensitivity should be treated as gently as possible: no scrubbing or pulling. Applications should be done with pressure techniques which help firm up the skin and vary depending on the type of product used. What's important? Never displace the skin tissue using rough gestures.

I use my mother's cream, is this bad?
If it's an occasional or a last minute solution it's not bad for you. But you will soon realize in listening to your skin, that the skin needs of mothers and daughters are not the same. Your mother's products may be too rich for you.

If I always use the same cream, will it become less effective?
Cells renew themselves constantly... There is no risk of your skin getting accustomed to the same cream!
Every day, new cells benefit from the active elements of a care product. If, after 28 days (the average time of complete cellular renewal), you see no effects (big or small) of your regular skin care product, change the product! When you've found the "right" one, you notice the benefits to your skin every day. And it shows!

I can't always tell whether my skin is dry or oily.
It's simple, oily skin tends to shine. Being thicker, it requires cleansing treatments starting in the morning. Dry skin is thin, with tiny wrinkles, it "pulls" and often results in a sensation of discomfort.

Does how thickly I apply the product determine its effectiveness on dry skin?
No, that was true 50 years ago! Today, thanks to advances in the field of cosmetology, it's possible to have a light and yet effective treatment for dry skin.

Exfoliating and masks

Is exfoliating advisable on mature and/or dry skin?
Regularly exfoliated skin is skin where wrinkles won't settle in. Contrary to conventional wisdom, the drier the skin the greater the need to exfoliate, because, while activating cell regeneration, exfoliation also titillates the sebaceous glands, which helps moisturize the skin. Ideal use: 2-3 times a week. However, with oily skin, once a week is enough so as not to over excite the already active sebaceous glands. For mature and sensitive skin, use an exfoliating cream or an enzyme peeling product.

Why use a mask since I exfoliate my skin regularly?
Exfoliation removes dead skin cells and improves the continuity of the epidermis. It's a product that works on the surface. A mask, acting like a bath, bathes cells in active elements that shine, soften, comfort and firm according to the skin's needs. You can add a drop of oil to your mask to promote good penetration into the layers of the epidermis. A mask, more effective after an exfoliation, enhances the performance of the day/night cream applied afterwards.

How do I prepare my skin for the change in seasons?
Increase use of exfoliation and choose a serum adapted to your needs. Apply a mask every day for a week, during breakfast for example.

Serums

What's a serum?

It is a concentrate of care, an efficiency booster, which is applied before the day or night cream. It optimizes the impregnation of the cream into the skin and the action of the active ingredients. Serums, designed to target specialized needs, act according to the needs of the skin on the functions responsible for youth or restore natural moisture or contribute to the firmness or skin balance mechanisms. They guarantee the beauty and strength of the epidermis.

Can I apply two serums at the same time?

Yes, no problem, thanks to the extra-fine instantly penetrating nature of this treatment. But apply the "simplest" serum first. For example, always start with moisturizing serum then follow up with the firming serum.

Why aren't serums used on their own?

Because a serum does not replace the hydrating and protecting actions of your cream, but serves to optimize them. If your serum has an anti-wrinkle control element, it's best to use it at night, because that's when cell regeneration is most active.

Make-up removal

After a lotion make-up remover, is another product necessary?

Ideally you should rinse your face with water and then apply a tonic which will eliminate the last traces of remover and also apply softening and toning elements to the epidermis.

What is the ideal recipe for healthy skin?

To ensure that you fully cleanse your skin, it is important that you complement your daily make-up remover with a water based foaming cleanser once or twice a week. Imagine if you only used cleansing lotion and tonic on your body. You would eventually need to wash it. The same thing applies to your face. There's nothing better for cleaning your face than a gentle foaming cleanser. It also comes in a formula for dry skin. You can also use a small soft gentle brush, to remove any remaining impurities. Your skin will be clearer and have a healthy glow.

Do I need a specialized product for removing eye make-up, and why?

Yes, you do need a specialized product to remove eye make-up; one that will dissolve mascara, waterproof or not, powder and eyeliner gently. The way you cleanse is equally as important for preserving the quality and resilience of your lashes. Don't rub, be delicate.

What purpose do preservatives serve in products?
They limit microbial growth (bacteria, fungus, yeast ...) in cosmetic products and are approved by various regulatory bodies (European Commission, FDA ...).

Eye care

Why use a specialized eye contour product?
Because the skin, in this area, is thinner and more delicate than the rest of the face and has no sebaceous glands. Contour care products contain very little fatty elements so as not to induce swelling.
So be careful not to "bring" your face products up to your eye contours because repeated swelling causes the skin to stretch and thus wrinkle more easily.

Bags, circles, wrinkles... what do I use?
Ideally you should apply a decongesting gel or a lifting serum in the morning and a special eye contour nourishing cream at night. Pat, don't rub; that will better moisturize the area and improve blood and lymphatic circulation. If you're prone to getting dark circles, keep your products in the refrigerator to reap the benefit of the cold.

Can I use my eye contour product around my lips?
Yes you can, but why would you want to? We want our eye contours to be smooth, sleek, and tight and our lips full.
If you are (were) a smoker and you have bar code wrinkles around your lips, you're better off using a product specifically designed for lip wrinkles.

The sun

When is skin most vulnerable to the sun?
When you are pregnant or under treatment (medical or hormonal), your skin becomes more sensitive to the sun.

In the summer, can I replace my regular day cream with a face sunscreen?
Yes, so choose a wrinkle sunscreen with SPF adapted, to give your skin protection, hydration and comfort.

Do I need sun protection if I'm wearing a hat?
Yes you do! A hat will protect your head and put some shade on your face but not enough for you to do without sunscreen!

General questions

Why isn't there one product that does everything?
Because synergistically, it's impossible for any single product to contain all of the active ingredients necessary for all the needs involved. However, it is possible to layer products, according to their functions and textures. For example, always apply a serum before a day or night cream to maximize its performance enhancing qualities. The textures are also complementary.

Why is a woman's skin more delicate than a man's?
Because thanks to testosterone (the male hormone), a man's skin is 20% thicker, richer in collagen and firmer than that of a woman. Better hydrated and better toned, it stays younger longer (but when ageing sets in it progresses more rapidly). It's oilier (men's sebaceous glands produce about twice as much sebum as women's) so prone to larger pores and more blackheads and pimples.

What do I do when I have a blackhead?
Apply a product especially designed for oily skin several nights in a row to soften it. To remove the "head" of blackheads, clean the area with a foaming cleanser using a soft brush.

What do I do when I have a pimple?
Avoid touching it! Cover it every night with a purifying mask or specialized product. And don't worry, even if it's all you think others see of you.

Your body

Can I use two body lotions at the same time or should I use them one after the other?
It depends on what beauty treatment you want, the results you're looking for and how much time you have available.

If you have time:
- while wet, exfoliate your body (including your breasts);
- shower with a moisturizing cleanser that neutralizes the harmful effects of hard water on the skin;
- apply oil to wet skin + (re)shower with cold water: the active ingredients of the oil will not only moisturize and soften the skin, but also relax, invigorate and detoxify;
And/or:
- on dry skin, apply slimming, firming, moisturizing or relaxing products as needed;
- finish up with an energizing rub down.

For those who don't have time:
- exfoliate with a homemade exfoliating body cleanser made by mixing your exfoliant with your cleanser;
- take a cool shower;

- moisturize with a homemade body cream created from adding a few drops of oil to your moisturizer; apply to dry skin.

For those who divide things up:
- for your legs and thighs, a slimming or anti-cellulite product;
- for your tummy, a tummy-waist toning product;
- for your arms, a firming or moisturizing product;
- for your breasts, a product that brightens, shapes and firms.

Can I apply anti-cellulite products anywhere on my body?
Yes, why not, if your skin has a dimpled appearance. But if it just lacks firmness, use slimming and firming products instead. And don't forget to exercise regularly, it is the best way to facilitate drainage and elimination.

What can I do about cellulite?
If you have a tendency to retain water in your legs, mix a detoxifying product together with both a draining and an anti-cellulite product so as to invigorate both blood and lymphatic circulation. If you have cellulite without water retention, an anti-cellulite cream should suffice.
In either case, regular application is the key (apply once or twice a day), together with a specialized slimming application method (rub upwards using your fist on the areas with cellulite).

How do I firm up my body?
No mystery here, a new way of life:
- work out regularly using targeted exercises
- finish your shower systematically with a jet of cold water from head to toe.
- exfoliate your body once or twice a week.

Is it important to massage when applying an anti-cellulite cream?
Yes, because it's all connected to the blood circulation. Massage improves the conversion of oxygen and the areas of poor blood flow. Slimming creams are usually thick which aids the effects of the massage, which is always done from the bottom up to facilitate drainage and elimination by the kidneys.

Make-up

I cleanse everyday but my skin is losing its luminescence: what's going on?
Maybe cleansing is not enough. We recommend cleaning your skin once or twice a
week with a water based foaming cleanser. Remember to exfoliate your skin at least
once a week. Both cleansing and moisturizing are crucial. Maybe your daily care
treatment is no longer right for your skin and can no longer assure smooth, glowing
comfortable skin.

Does make-up protect your skin or preventing it from breathing?
Putting on make-up is like getting dressed to go out! Yes, make-up does protect your
skin from damaging rays of the sun, the wind and grime… Use a foundation with
SPF to protect the skin from outside irritants and from the sun even in town.

Can my skin tan under my foundation?
Be careful, foundation (certainly one without SPF) cannot provide a sunscreen.
Some rays still get through and you can get burned. If you want to sit in the sun,
the best thing to do is to put on a sunscreen under your make-up or use a
foundation with an SPF to get some nice colour. Remember to refresh your
sunscreen every 2 hours!

How do I choose a foundation?
Select three shades close to your natural skin color. Apply a small amount of each
on the inside of your wrist or on the lower part of your face: choose the one that
blends in most naturally with your skin colour.

What's the difference between a BB Cream and a CC Cream?
A *Blemish Base* cream is a treating foundation that moisturizes, protects, corrects
imperfections and evens out skin texture. A Colour Control cream covers and works
more on differences in colouring.

7
A STAR, EVEN
ON THE ROAD

So as to be able to make yourself beautiful on all means of transport, prepare the ideal vanity case!

By plane

Checklist!

- ☐ facial spray
- ☐ bottle of water, bought after the security check points
- ☐ tired legs cream
- ☐ compression stockings
- ☐ moisturizing cream
- ☐ eye contour cream
- ☐ foundation
- ☐ mascara
- ☐ lip gloss

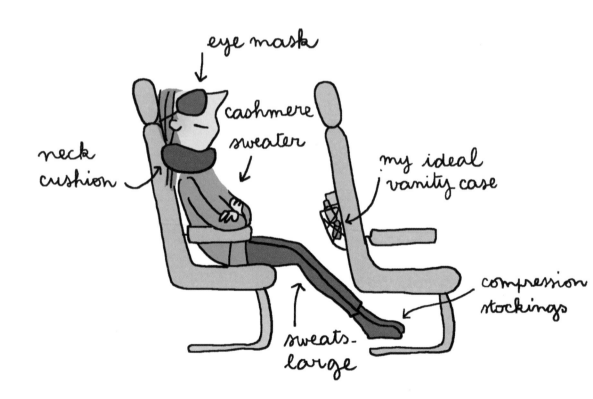

Do's

- Take a cold shower in the morning to prepare your legs better for depressurization.
- Apply your tired legs, refreshing and energizing care product.
- Put on your compression stockings just after applying the leg care product to keep it fresh.
- Prepare a beauty kit to redo your treatment and make-up before landing.
- Take an aspirin in order to thin the blood before you leave if you're prone to swelling.
- Reapply a bit of your leg care product on top of the stockings regularly during long flights.
- Boost lymphatic circulation by regularly rotating your ankles and flexing your calves. Also every once in a while squeeze your legs gently from your ankles to your knees using both hands.
- Drink enough to offset the dry air and improve blood circulation.
- Remove your make-up and apply moisturizer and your eye contour product when flying overnight.
- When you wake up, before applying your make-up, moisturize your face again.
- Once you've reached your destination, put your legs up (against a wall for example), take a cold shower and sleep with your legs elevated.

Don'ts

- Avoid wearing tight or uncomfortable clothing. Leave your high heels in your luggage and wear shoes that are more like "slippers". If necessary, carry on a second set of clothes to change into before you land.
- Don't travel hungry: eat a light meal before the flight, even if it means passing on the in-flight meal or the sweet and/or savory snacks later on.
- Avoid alcohol and soft drinks.
- Do not cross your legs during the flight so as to avoid impeding the venous return.
- Try not to stay seated the whole length of the flight. Stretch your legs regularly by walking up and down the aisle to revive the circulatory system that has a tendency to stagnate when sitting for extended periods of time.
- Avoid tight stockings or socks which compress the leg, block blood flow and cause swelling.
- Avoid wearing your contact lenses during long flights. The dry air could dry your eyes.

By car

Checklist!

❏ cooling spray or water care product. In addition to waking up your face, it'll also perfume your car!
❏ eye contour gel. To apply every 2 hours during a long journey to help you stay awake and attentive.
❏ sun screen... because the sun's rays pass through the windshield. Don't forget to protect your hands from the sun.
❏ bottle of water to hydrate yourself regularly

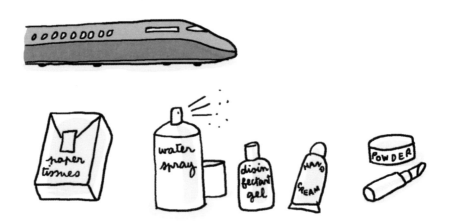

By train

Checklist!

❏ paper tissues
❏ cooling water spray to refresh yourself whenever you need it
❏ sanitizing gel
❏ hand cream
❏ powder and a lipstick for touch-ups before arriving

Why do my legs swell when I'm on a plane?

faq 59 Oxygen in an airplane in flight is not the same as it is at sea level, and can lead to hypoxia (decreased oxygen levels in the blood). Add this to a slowdown in the venous return linked to prolonged immobility and it's no surprise that your legs swell.

What effect does jet lag have on my skin?

faq 60 Your skin is often dehydrated and weakened when you are in a different time zone; this is often due to the depressurization and dry air from the plane. Remember to moisturize well before takeoff, during the flight and before landing. To better withstand jet-lag, which throws off your internal clock, adapt your diet:
-the night before you leave, go for the carbohydrates (such as pasta). These suppliers of tryptophan (an amino acid important in the composition of proteins) allow the brain to develop serotonin, a neurotransmitter that promotes sleep.
-The day after you arrive, eat a protein-rich meal to put your brain into 'awake' mode.

And biking

Checklist!

☐ water with some lemon so it's more thirst-quenching
☐ small towel or refreshing wipes
☐ sunscreen to be applied before you set off, and refreshed every 2 hours on exposed areas from head to toe, without forgetting the neck and the ears

Acknowledgements:

Thanks to my family, my daughters, my nieces,
Dominique Rist, Isabelle Fromager and especially
Jacques Courtin, my father, who continuously inspired
me throughout the writing of this book.

Printed in Spain by Macrolibros
Registered copyright: October 2014

8866749 / 3010000048343

80005713
ISBN 978-2-9550166-1-9